Vocabulary 3

For Young Catholics

WRITTEN BY
SETON STAFF

SETON PRESS
FRONT ROYAL, VA

Editors: Seton Staff
Illustrator: Benjamin Hatke

Seton Home Study School
1350 Progress Drive
Front Royal, VA 22630
540-636-9990
540-636-1602 fax

For more information, visit us on the Web at http://www.setonhome.org.
Contact us by e-mail at info@setonhome.org.

ISBN: 978-1-60704-121-4

Cover: Stained glass window of St. John the Evangelist

DEDICATED TO THE SACRED HEART OF JESUS

VOCABULARY 3 FOR YOUNG CATHOLICS

CONTENTS

VOCABULARY 3
INTRODUCTION

Some parents are surprised that Seton has a vocabulary series as part of our regular program. This is an academic area that needs special attention because, unlike in past generations, students are not reading as much as they should.

With a lack of reading comes a lack of thinking. Unlike the television and the computer, a book encourages learning new words and new ideas.

At Seton, we are dedicated to helping children develop their thinking and analytical skills. These skills can be improved dramatically by learning to use new vocabulary words.

This vocabulary book was written by a homeschooling mom and edited by a homeschooling dad who is an experienced teacher of third graders in a Catholic school. Many of the words our Seton students likely know already, but we hope that besides knowing the words, our students will use the words in their conversations.

We hope your child will enjoy the colorful pictures, interesting sentences, and crossword puzzles contained in the lessons of this *Vocabulary 3* workbook.

A dictionary can be very interesting to teach the use of words in different ways. Most of the children's dictionaries have colorful pictures. Consider having your child spend 15 minutes a day looking through a dictionary. Choose one word for the week to use as often as possible. This does not need to be assigned during "class" time.

Your child should read every day, and we strongly urge you to read to your child as well. If your child finds a word he does not know, ask him to ask you or to look for it in the dictionary. Encourage your child not to simply read past a word he does not know. Give your child a small reward for either asking you the meaning of a word, guessing the meaning of the word based on context, or for finding unknown words in the dictionary!

Consider purchasing a thesaurus. Help your child to become familiar with common synonyms and antonyms. Look on a search engine for *"Words Every Third Grader Should Know"* and for *"Free Vocabulary Games for Children."*

We hope that you and your child have fun with *Vocabulary 3 for Young Catholics*.

The Virgin of Hope, by Juan Sariñena

Lesson 1: Word List

greedy   drizzle   whirlpool   copperhead   heron

weasel   eel   torch   station   tower

<u>Greedy</u> *(adj)* **is wanting something too much, especially if it is more than** **needed.** The child was so **greedy** that he ate all the Christmas cookies.

A <u>torch</u> *(n)* **is a stick with burning material on one end that is lit and carried for light.** As he entered the dark cave, the explorer lit his **torch**.

A <u>weasel</u> *(n)* **is a small animal, about a foot long with a slender body and a tail with a black tip.**

That **weasel** likes to wander around our chicken coop to find eggs to eat.

A <u>copperhead</u> *(n)* **is a kind of poisonous snake, about three feet long, with a copper-colored head.** That **copperhead** slithered through the grass in the woods.

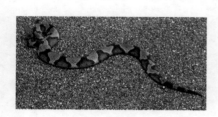

<u>Drizzle</u> *(n)* **is gentle rain.** We will pray to St. Isidore for a **drizzle** during the dry weather.

A <u>station</u> *(n)* **is a place used for people to gather for a special purpose, such as a gas station or railroad station.** Grandma is coming to visit us, but we must pick her up at the train **station**.

An <u>eel</u> *(n)* **is a long, slippery fish, shaped like a snake.** The children screamed and swam away when they saw an **eel** moving through the water.

A <u>heron</u> *(n)* **is a wading bird with long legs, a long neck, and a long bill; it hunts for fish.** The **heron** landed in the lake where we were fishing.

A <u>whirlpool</u> *(n)* **is water that flows around and around quickly.** A large **whirlpool** in a river or the ocean can be dangerous for swimmers.

A <u>tower</u> *(n)* **is a high structure; may form part of a church, castle, or other building.** The bell high up in the church **tower** rang out before the beginning of Sunday Mass.

Puzzle

Choose a word from the word list to solve the crossword puzzle.

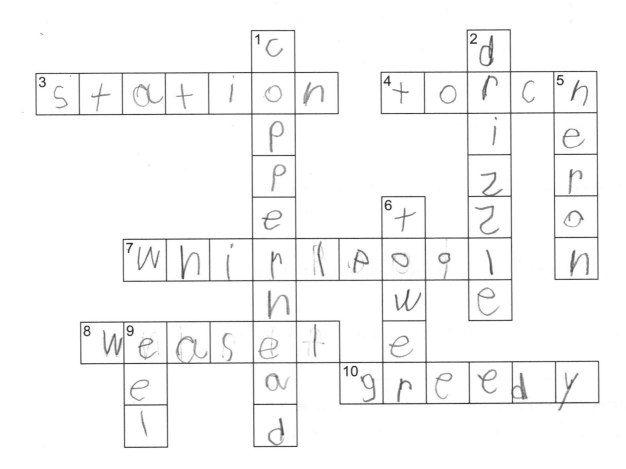

ACROSS

3 place used for a special purpose

4 a stick lit on one end

7 water flowing in a circle

8 a small animal with a slender body

10 wanting something too much

DOWN

1 a poisonous snake

2 what farmers would like in dry weather

5 a wading bird with long legs

6 a high structure

9 fish that looks like a snake

Fill-in-the-Blanks

Fill in the blank with a word from the word list.

The hungry _ caught a rat behind the barn.	1. cat
The _ raised his copper-colored head out of the grass.	2. copper head
My uncle carried a _ to help him see inside the old dark mine.	3. torch
King Midas was very _ and wanted more and more gold.	4. Greedy
The big _ lifted its head feathers and dived into the water.	5. Heron
Tom dropped a leaf into the small _ and watched it go round and round until it was sucked under the water.	6. WHirlPool
The rain was heavy this morning, but in the afternoon, it became just a _ .	7. drizzle
While swimming, Lily saw a long _ , but it slithered away when she screamed!	8.
Dad tried to find a gas _ for his car on the way to the Rosary Rally.	9. station
The tall church _ was made of brick and had a golden cross at the top.	10. tower

Word Usage

Circle the letter next to the sentence that uses the word correctly.

1. (a) The cathedral **tower** was so high that it looked like it touched the sky.
   (b) We will use the **tower** to dig up the garden.

2. (a) The **whirlpool** blew the kite far away into the clouds above.
   (b) A small **whirlpool** formed after the rainstorm and sucked in our pile of leaves.

3 (a) Judas was so **greedy** for money that he betrayed Our Lord.
   (b) Mother told me that the **greedy** bush was green.

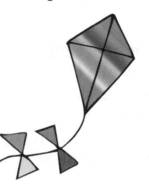

4. (a) When you are sixteen, you can **drizzle** the car.
   (b) The **drizzle** was very light, but we still used an umbrella.

5. (a) My mother told me to **torch** my sister home.
   (b) Without the **torch**, Dad could not see where he was going.

6. (a) The **heron** put his beak in the water, ready to catch a fish for his dinner.
   (b) Can you **heron** what I am saying?

7. (a) My boat became all tangled in the **weasel**.
   (b) The **weasel** scampered away as soon as I came close.

8. (a) The **copperhead's** tan color allows it to blend in with the dirt.
   (b) After dinner, I rinsed the **copperheads** and put them in the dishwasher.

9. (a) Mother told me that I had to **station** home after nine o'clock.
   (b) Have you ever been to the train **station** near St. Patrick's Church?

10. (a) The **eel** of the shoe was very smooth.
    (b) Usually an **eel** lives in the shallow waters of the ocean.

Lesson 2: Word List

raft	ladder	bishop	cherry	eager
opossum	arrow	canary	jacket	flute

A **raft** *(n)* is a flat structure, usually made of logs, which floats like a boat. St. Anthony's cloak, acting like a **raft**, miraculously carried him across the river.

An **opossum** *(n)* is a small animal the size of a cat, with a pointed nose and a long, skinny tail; lives in trees; if scared, pretends to be dead. My dog's bark scared the **opossum** and caused it to run up into the tree.

A **ladder** *(n)* is an object used for climbing, with a set of steps fastened to two long sides, usually made of wood or metal. Dad climbed the **ladder** to fix the gutter on the roof.

An **arrow** *(n)* is a slender, pointed stick which is shot from a bow. An old friend pulled the **arrow** out of St. Sebastian so he did not die.

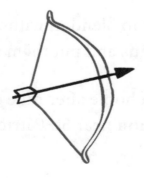

A **bishop** *(n)* is a priest chosen by the pope to be in charge of many Catholic parishes. St. Nicholas, a **bishop** of long ago, was very kind to children.

A **canary** *(n)* is a songbird with yellow feathers. Helen's pet **canary** likes to sing while sitting on its perch.

A **cherry** *(n)* is a small, red, sweet fruit with a pit in the middle. I like to put a **cherry** on top of my ice cream.

A **jacket** *(n)* is a short coat. I wore my green **jacket** to church because it was very chilly outside.

To be **eager** *(adj)* is to have much interest or desire. St. Imelda was **eager** to receive Jesus in Holy Communion.

A **flute** *(n)* is a long, slender musical instrument, played by blowing in a hole on one side; different notes are made by covering holes with the fingers. Dick enjoys playing the **flute** in the orchestra.

Choose a word from the word list to solve the crossword puzzle.

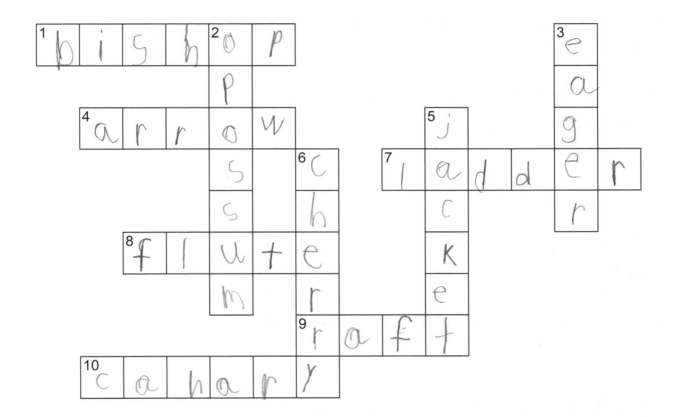

ACROSS

1 a priest in charge of several parishes
4 a small, pointed stick shot from a bow
7 an object used for climbing
8 a long, slender musical instrument
9 a flat boat
10 a songbird with yellow feathers

DOWN

2 a small animal that lives in trees
3 having much desire
5 a short coat
6 a small, round fruit with a pit in the middle

Fill-in-the-Blanks

Fill in the blank with a word from the word list.

It was getting very cold outside, so John ran into the house to get his _ .	1. jacket
We saw an _ lying upside down in the woods, but he was just playing dead!	2. opossum
I was lucky to meet the _ when he came to our church for the Confirmation.	3. bishop
St. Nicholas once climbed up a _ and dropped a bag of money through a poor man's chimney.	4. ladder
When our small boat sank on the lake, Dad and I made a _ out of some logs.	5. Raft
My uncle and I planted a _ tree next to the apple tree.	6. cherry
In the movie, Robin Hood shoots his _ while spinning in the air.	7. arrow
Little Regina was _ to open her Christmas gift wrapped in bright red paper!	8. eager
The bright, yellow _ chirped so loudly that it woke up the girls.	9. canary
Jacinta liked to dance to the quick music of her brother's _ .	10. flute

Word Usage

Replace the words in bold with the correct word from the word list.

I brought my **pretty yellow songbird** to the hospital, and it sang to my sick friend.	1. canary
I prayed to St. Cecilia to help me play well on my **long, slender musical instrument**.	2. flute
Robin Hood was a great shot with a **pointed stick shot from a bow.**	3. arrow
A **priest in charge of many parishes** will say the Confirmation Mass tomorrow.	4. bishop
The boys made a **floating framework of logs** to cross the river.	5. raft
My brother gave his **short coat** to a poor, shivering little boy.	6. jacket
Catherine put a **small, round, red fruit** on the birthday cake.	7. cherry
The painter almost fell off the **object used for climbing** because it was such a windy day.	8. ladder
The boys were **having much desire** to go on the camping trip with Dad!	9. eager
That hole in the tree could be the home of a **small animal that lives in trees.**	10. opossum

fasten	antenna	badger	gnat	herd
chipmunk	bamboo	kite	nutcracker	candle

To <u>fasten</u> *(v)* is to join or to attach firmly in place or to something else. Always <u>fasten</u> your seat belt!

A <u>kite</u> *(n)* is a very light, wooden frame covered with paper or cloth. My brother is flying his big, blue <u>kite</u>.

A <u>chipmunk</u> *(n)* is a very small, striped animal related to the squirrel. The four-inch-long <u>chipmunk</u> grabbed the seeds and ran up the tree.

A <u>gnat</u> *(n)* is a tiny, two-winged insect. That nasty <u>gnat</u> keeps flying in my face!

An <u>antenna</u> *(n)* is a feeler on the head of an insect; an insect has two of these, one on each side. Susie could see the bug's <u>antenna</u> moving back and forth.

A <u>nutcracker</u> *(n)* is an object for cracking the shells of nuts. I used my <u>nutcracker</u> to open the walnuts Grandma brought for Christmas.

<u>Bamboo</u> *(n)* is a treelike plant, very tall and stiff with hollow stems, used for making canes, flutes, guitars, and furniture. My dad bought a chair made of <u>bamboo</u>.

A <u>herd</u> *(n)* is a large group of animals, such as cows and horses, that live together. The shepherd led his <u>herd</u> of sheep to fresh water.

A <u>badger</u> *(n)* is a hairy, fierce, gray animal, about fifteen inches long, with short legs and a long face with three white stripes; lives in holes it digs for itself. That <u>badger</u> in our yard dug tunnels all around the barn.

A <u>candle</u> *(n)* is a stick of wax with a wick in the center, which burns to give light. Before electric lights, students read by the light of a <u>candle</u>.

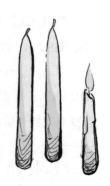

Puzzle

Sept 11

Choose a word from the word list to solve the crossword puzzle.

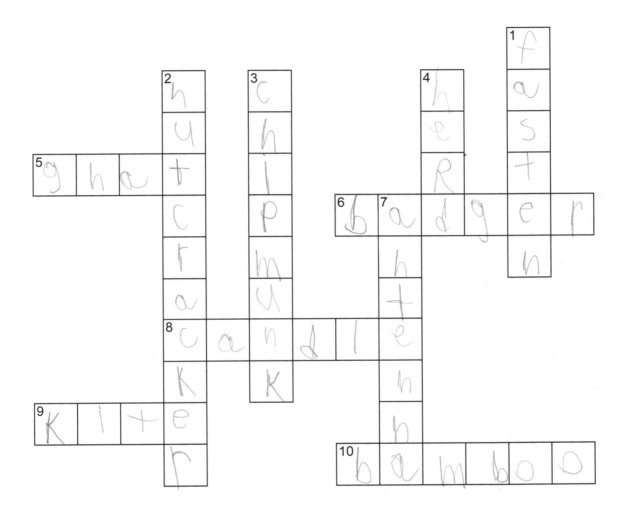

ACROSS

5 a bothersome insect
6 an animal that digs holes in the ground
8 a stick of wax which burns to give light
9 a light, wooden frame covered with paper
10 a stiff treelike plant

DOWN

1 to attach firmly to something
2 an object for cracking the shells of nuts
3 a very small, striped animal which eats seeds
4 large group of animals, such as cattle
7 an insect's feeler

Fill-in-the-Blanks

Fill in the blank with a word from the word list.

I always _ my coat buttons before I go outside in the snow.	1. fasteh
While my brother was flying his _ , it became tangled in a tree.	2. Kite
Catherine lit a _ at the small shrine and prayed for her sick brother.	3. candle
This _ is excellent for opening walnuts!	4. nutcRackeR
My brother brought a _ flute from the Philippines.	5. bamboo
The _ buzzed around my face, bothering me while I weeded the garden.	6. Ghat
Some wild squirrels and a _ ate the nuts from St. Francis' hand.	7. chipmunk
The prodigal son had a job taking care of a _ of pigs.	8. herd
The poor insect had only one _ to feel its way around.	9. antenna
The other day, Nina found a _ running into a hole in the backyard.	10. badger

Word Usage

Circle the letter next to the sentence that uses the word correctly.

1. (a) Mother spanked us for being **badger** at the park.
   (b) The boys did not see the **badger** because its fur color blended with the dirt.

2. (a) The policemen will **fasten** their medals to their shirts.
   (b) John won the race because he was the **fasten**.

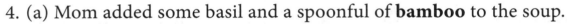

3. (a) Mike received a coin collecting **kite** for his birthday.
   (b) Many a family brought a **kite** to the field on that windy day.

4. (a) Mom added some basil and a spoonful of **bamboo** to the soup.
   (b) My grandfather made this **bamboo** chair more than five years ago.

5. (a) The baby **chipmunk** ran quickly under the porch steps.
   (b) Our dog is a mix of Labrador, sheep dog, and **chipmunk**.

6. (a) That **nutcracker** with cheese was very tasty.
   (b) Mom used a **nutcracker** to open the nuts in the gift basket.

7. (a) The farmer grew a large **candle** to sell at the market.
   (b) The pastor decorated a large white **candle** for the Easter vigil Mass.

8. (a) Using a microscope, she was able to see the **antenna** on the insect.
   (b) You can see better if you put on this **antenna**.

9. (a) A good shepherd takes care of each sheep in his **herd**.
   (b) I rinsed and dried the **herd** and put them on the shelf.

10. (a) "Why does this **gnat** keep flying in my face?"
    (b) "Put the books away and go take your **gnat**."

Lesson 4: Word List

| visor | poet | trade | doubt | weapon |
| crucifix | crate | creek | haul | magnet |

A <u>visor</u> *(n)* is the movable front part of a helmet that covers the face; the brim of a cap. The knight pulled down his <u>visor</u> before facing the enemy.

A <u>crucifix</u> *(n)* is a cross with the figure of Jesus Christ crucified on it. After confession, James prayed before the large <u>crucifix</u> in the church.

A <u>poet</u> *(n)* is a person who writes poems. Her favorite poem is called "Prayer" written by a monk who was a <u>poet</u>.

A <u>crate</u> *(n)* is a large box made of wood used for shipping or storing things. We shipped a <u>crate</u> of tropical fruit to our cousins in Canada.

To <u>trade</u> *(v)* is to exchange things. Katie and Anna like to <u>trade</u> holy cards.

A <u>creek</u> *(n)* is a small stream of water. When the water froze in the <u>creek</u>, the boys went ice skating on it.

To <u>doubt</u> *(v)* is to feel unsure; to refuse to believe. St. Thomas the Apostle would <u>doubt</u> that Jesus had risen from the dead.

To <u>haul</u> *(v)* means to pull or drag. Our Lord was forced to <u>haul</u> His heavy cross up the hill of Calvary.

A <u>weapon</u> *(n)* is an object used for fighting, such as a sword, spear, arrow, or gun. St. Michael is often pictured with a spear for his <u>weapon</u>.

A <u>magnet</u> *(n)* is iron that attracts other bits of iron or steel. The Christmas holy card on our refrigerator is being held by a <u>magnet</u>.

Puzzle

Choose a word from the word list to solve the crossword puzzle.

ACROSS

2 to pull or drag
6 brim of a cap
8 to exchange things
9 object used for fighting
10 to feel unsure

DOWN

1 cross with figure of Jesus
3 person who writes poems
4 box of wood for shipping
5 small stream of water
7 attracts iron or steel

Fill-in-the-Blanks

Fill in the blank with a word from the word list.

My aunts _ they will be able to visit us at Christmas because of the snowstorm.	1.
A knight would pray all night, laying his _ , usually a sword, before the altar.	2.
Mary hung a _ in every room of our new house to remind us of Jesus' sacrifice.	3.
In our science experiment, we used a _ to attract paper clips and nails.	4.
Timmy was so excited to see a large _ with his name on it in the delivery truck!	5.
My brother's cap had a _ with a picture of our church on it.	6.
The apostles struggled to _ the heavy fishing net after Jesus multiplied the fish.	7.
The early American pilgrims began to _ useful tools with the Indians.	8.
Long ago, singing minstrels and a _ would entertain the king with songs and poems.	9.
After the heavy rain, our nearby _ almost overflowed.	10.

Word Usage

Circle the letter next to the sentence that uses the word correctly.

1. (a) Mix the cookie dough on the **crate** and put it into the oven.
   (b) Our family filled a **crate** with food for families after the hurricane.

2. (a) We will **doubt** a cheese sandwich for lunch.
   (b) I **doubt** it will rain today, since the clouds are clearing.

3. (a) The spilled nails were easy to collect by attracting them with a **magnet**.
   (b) We could see the moon and the stars very closely through the **magnet**.

4. (a) We made a little altar with a statue of the Blessed Mother and a **crucifix**.
   (b) Fold your hands together in a **crucifix** when you pray.

5. (a) Set the table, Anna; **poet** the fork on the left, and the knife on the right.
   (b) The **poet** wrote a poem for the pope on his birthday.

6. (a) St. Dominic was given the rosary as a holy **weapon** against the enemies of the
       Catholic Church.
   (b) After the death of her cat, Susan spent the afternoon **weapon**.

7. (a) Jim put his glasses on the **visor** of his cap before looking through the binoculars.
   (b) The waiter at court set the **visor** full of wine before the king.

8. (a) We will **trade** fruits from our orchards for milk from the dairy farm.
   (b) Mark was sent on an errand to **trade** the trash to the dump.

9. (a) St. Paul visited the faithful on the island of **creek**.
   (b) The boys walked across the **creek**, stepping carefully on each stone.

10. (a) Mother had me **haul** the garbage down to the dump.
    (b) The wedding was held in a beautiful **haul**.

Lesson 5: Word List

collect	halo	donkey	author	rapidly
chapter	weep	rainbow	hummingbird	traitor

To <u>collect</u> (v) is to gather or put together. I <u>collect</u> old postage stamps.

To <u>weep</u> (v) is to cry or shed tears. "Please do not <u>weep</u>; we will find your lost kitten."

A <u>halo</u> (n) is a ring of light drawn or painted around the head of a saint. The artist painted a gold <u>halo</u> over the head of St. Joseph.

A <u>rainbow</u> (n) is an arch of several colors seen in the sky after a rain; red, orange, yellow, green, blue, and violet are rainbow colors. God set the <u>rainbow</u> in the sky as a promise to Noah.

A <u>donkey</u> (n) is an animal like a horse except smaller, with longer ears; tends to be a stubborn animal. The <u>donkey</u> gently carried Mary and Baby Jesus to Egypt.

A <u>hummingbird</u> (n) is a very small, brightly colored bird with narrow wings that makes a humming sound. The wings of a <u>hummingbird</u> move so rapidly, we cannot see them.

An <u>author</u> (n) is a person who writes books. St. Luke is the <u>author</u> of the Acts of the Apostles in the Bible.

A <u>traitor</u> (n) is a person who betrays his country or his friends. There is no greater <u>traitor</u> than Judas who betrayed Jesus.

A <u>chapter</u> (n) is a part of a book that separates different parts of the book. Matt read the first <u>chapter</u> of that book in only five minutes!

<u>Rapidly</u> (adv) means fast, quickly, swiftly. The Shenandoah River moves <u>rapidly</u> over the dam below the cliff.

Puzzle

Choose a word from the word list to solve the crossword puzzle.

ACROSS

1 ring of light around the head of a saint
4 arch of colors seen in the sky
5 section that separates parts of a book
6 person who betrays his friends
7 animal like a horse but smaller

DOWN

1 very small, brightly colored bird
2 person who writes books
3 to gather together
4 very quickly or swiftly

Fill-in-the-Blanks

Fill in the blank with a word from the word list.

The _ of the book *Our Lady of Fatima* is Father Lovasik.	1.
John, are you reading a _ in the Gospel of Mark in the Bible?	2.
Our parish is trying to _ cans of food for Thanksgiving for poor families.	3.
The _ is a sign of God's promise to Noah not to flood the Earth again.	4.
Aunt Rose watched a beautiful _ flying around the garden.	5.
My family walked _ to church so we would be on time for Mass.	6.
The Americans learned that the soldier was a _ .	7.
Maria painted the _ of the Blessed Mother with gold paint.	8.
Jesus said to the women of Jerusalem, "Do not _ for Me but for your children."	9.
Jesus rode on a _ through the streets of Jerusalem while people placed palms on the road before Him.	10.

Word Usage

Replace the words in bold with the correct word from the word list.

I met the **person who writes books** for a great Catholic book company.	1.
This **very small, brightly colored bird** can beat its wings eighty times per second!	2.
The girls want to **gather** holy cards to put in a big scrapbook.	3.
Our Lady will **cry and shed tears** in sorrow if sinners keep wounding the Sacred Heart.	4.
The villain was a **person who betrayed us** who sold secrets to the enemy.	5.
Dad read a **part of the book** after dinner.	6.
An **animal like a horse** miraculously knelt before the Host carried by St. Anthony.	7.
Our little boat sailed **very quickly** to the other side of the river.	8.
After the thunderstorm ended, we saw a beautiful **arch of colors** in the sky.	9.
A **ring of light pictured around the head of a saint** reminds us of the light of grace given by God to the saints because of their holiness.	10.

Lesson 6: Word List

octopus	igloo	concert	stake	pure
hut	nibble	drill	resurrect	harp

An <u>octopus</u> *(n)* is a sea animal having a soft body and eight arms. The **octopus** wrapped itself around the big fish.

A <u>hut</u> *(n)* is a small, roughly-made house. St. Francis Xavier learned that a family in India usually lived in a **hut**.

An <u>igloo</u> *(n)* is an Eskimo home that is built of blocks of hard snow. An **igloo** is often shaped like a dome.

A <u>drill</u> *(n)* is a tool or machine used for making holes. Dad used a **drill** when he built the bookcase.

A <u>concert</u> *(n)* is a musical entertainment. Margaret played the violin at the pro-life **concert**.

To <u>nibble</u> *(v)* is to bite off very small pieces. The mouse began to **nibble** through the net to save the lion's life.

A <u>stake</u> *(n)* is a stick or post pointed at one end for driving into the ground. Dad pounded a **stake** into the ground to hold up each tomato plant.

To <u>resurrect</u> *(v)* is to come to life again or to bring back from the dead. The apostles did not understand that Jesus would **resurrect** after His death and burial.

<u>Pure</u> *(adj)* is clean, clear, or without sin. The heart of Mary remained **pure** and stainless all her life.

A <u>harp</u> *(n)* is a large, stringed musical instrument played with the fingers. In many paintings of St. Cecilia, she is shown playing a **harp**.

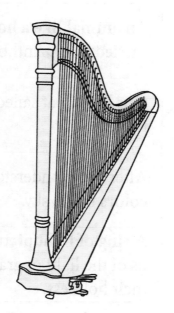

Puzzle

Choose a word from the word list to solve the crossword puzzle.

ACROSS

2 tool for making holes
4 small, roughly-made house
5 to bite small pieces
6 to rise from the dead
9 sea animal having eight arms

DOWN

1 musical entertainment
3 house built of hard snow
4 large stringed musical instrument
7 pointed stick
8 clean

Fill in the blank with a word from the word list.

My dad used a _ to make holes in the wood for building a table.	1.
Clare played a beautiful song on her golden _ at our cousin's wedding.	2.
We saw an _ and sharks at the sea aquarium.	3.
The boys like to _ on some cookies after lunch.	4.
The filter on the faucet makes the water _ .	5.
St. Elizabeth of Hungary cared for the poor family that lived in a _ nearby.	6.
When my dad was in Alaska, he ate some meals with an Eskimo family in an _ .	7.
St. Peter was given the power by Jesus to _ Tabitha who had died.	8.
The pear tree was falling, so we drove a _ into the ground and tied the tree to it.	9.
Peter and David played a duet on the piano at the _ .	10.

Word Usage

Replace the words in bold with the correct word from the word list.

The deep sea diver became entangled with an **eight-armed creature.**	1.
Lisa likes the beautiful music made by the strings of a **large stringed musical instrument.**	2.
Our family loves to go to the Christmas **musical entertainment** at St. John's Church Hall.	3.
The two sisters were shocked when Jesus called out for their dead brother to **come alive** from the tomb!	4.
Dad had to purchase a new **hole-making tool** to build the bookcase for our school books.	5.
Mom said we should eat our food properly and not **bite off tiny pieces** on the vegetables.	6.
When Grandpa came to this plain, he put up a **sharp post** every ten feet to mark off his farm property.	7.
The Husky dogs slept near the Eskimo's **home made of ice.**	8.
The lily is a symbol of the Blessed Mother's **sinless** soul.	9.
Father John lived in a **small shack** to work among the poor natives.	10.

Lesson 7: Word List

acrobat	vigil	blessing	hawk	medal
caterpillar	spoil	crow	shabby	oval

An **acrobat** *(n)* is a person who can dance on a rope or wire, and swing on a trapeze. The **acrobat** was riding a unicycle on a high wire in the circus!

A **caterpillar** *(n)* is a wormlike insect that has hatched from an egg; will change into a moth or butterfly. It is amazing to watch how a **caterpillar** changes into a colorful butterfly.

A **vigil** *(n)* is the eve of a religious feast day. We went to Mass on the **vigil** of the Assumption.

To **spoil** *(v)* is to damage, injure, or destroy. Do not **spoil** the surprise by telling her about the party.

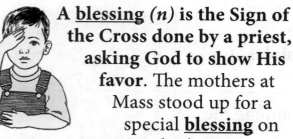

A **blessing** *(n)* is the Sign of the Cross done by a priest, asking God to show His favor. The mothers at Mass stood up for a special **blessing** on

IN THE NAME OF THE FATHER + Mother's Day.

To **crow** *(v)* is to make the loud cry of a rooster. Jesus predicted to Peter that he would deny Jesus before the cock would **crow**.

A **hawk** *(n)* is a bird of prey with a strong, hooked beak and large curved claws. The **hawk** can see a field mouse half a mile away.

Shabby *(adj)* means old and worn out. The old gentleman's suit looks **shabby** in the bright light.

A **medal** *(n)* is a small object made of metal with words on it; often given as a reward. The soldier received a gold **medal** for saving his friends during a battle.

Oval *(adj)* is having the shape of an egg. My mother wears the **oval** brooch she received on her wedding day.

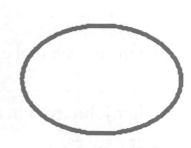

Puzzle

Choose a word from the word list to solve the crossword puzzle.

ACROSS

2 person who can dance on a rope
5 Sign of the Cross done by a priest
10 changes into a butterfly

DOWN

1 bird with a hooked beak and long, curved claws
3 shaped like an egg
4 eve of a religious feast
6 to injure or destroy
7 old and worn out
8 piece of metal given as a reward
9 to make a noise like a rooster

Fill-in-the-Blanks

Fill in the blank with a word from the word list.

The _ ate holes through our lettuce leaves.	1.
The boy's baseball uniform was _ , so his mother bought a new one.	2.
Betsy decorated the _ card so that it looked like an Easter egg.	3.
The Blessed Mother gave St. Catherine Labouré the design for a special _ with a picture of the Immaculate Virgin Mary.	4.
The children watched the _ do marvelous tricks on the trapeze at the circus.	5.
Our pastor gave the Ryan family a special _ , asking God to watch over them on their long trip.	6.
The Bible says that St. Peter wept when he heard a rooster _ three times.	7.
The rain will _ my plan to go to the park.	8.
We love to light the candles at the Easter _ .	9.
A big _ likes to sit on top of the telephone pole and watch for mice and squirrels to catch in his beak!	10.

Word Usage

Circle the letter next to the sentence that uses the word correctly.

1. (a) Father Brown gave all the children a **blessing**.
   (b) We asked mother to show us which **blessing** to buy.

2. (a) "Do not **medal** your clean clothes."
   (b) Katherine received a blessed **medal** as a reward for her religion answers.

3. (a) Julia's shell collection had round, **oval,** and triangle-shaped shells.
   (b) We poured some fresh **oval** water into all the jugs to make lemonade.

4. (a) The **acrobat** performed all sorts of amazing tricks on the trapeze.
   (b) We saw an **acrobat** flying around our shed last night.

5. (a) Yesterday, all the children played games and ran races at the **vigil**.
   (b) We prayed in the chapel on the **vigil** of the feast of the Assumption.

6. (a) That bird found a **caterpillar** and a worm to eat for his breakfast.
   (b) For the science experiment, we watched a **caterpillar** turn into a frog.

7. (a) That **hawk** built his nest high up in the tree.
   (b) "Add a **hawk** of ham to the soup after it boils," Mother said.

8. (a) If the wood does not burn in the fireplace, turn the logs with this **crow**.
   (b) That rooster will **crow** every morning at sunrise to wake you up!

9. (a) Kitty's favorite place to sit was by the fireplace on a **shabby**, red chair.
   (b) Timothy poured **shabby** water on the flowers in the garden.

10. (a) "Christine, don't **spoil** your nice dress playing in the mud."
    (b) I slipped on that **spoil** on the floor.

Lesson 8: Word List

| widow | stream | paste | mint | raw |
| monastery | virtue | needle | tremble | choir |

A <u>widow</u> *(n)* is a woman whose husband has died and who has not remarried. After the death of St. Joseph, Mary remained a <u>widow</u>.

A <u>monastery</u> *(n)* is a building where monks live. That <u>monastery</u> in Europe is hundreds of years old.

A <u>stream</u> *(n)* is a flow, usually of liquid or running water. After a rainfall, the water in the <u>stream</u> rises and flows much more quickly.

<u>Virtue</u> *(n)* is a habit of doing good; kindness is an example of a virtue. Katy learned about the <u>virtue</u> of charity at her Little Flowers club.

A <u>paste</u> *(n)* is a soft, smooth, thick mixture. The recipe said to add tomato <u>paste</u> to the chili.

A <u>needle</u> *(n)* is a tiny, slender metal tool, sharp at one end with a hole or eye in the other end, used for sewing. Betsy Ross used a <u>needle</u> and thread to sew the American flag.

<u>Mint</u> *(n)* is a sweet-smelling herb used for flavoring food or candy. I put a little <u>mint</u> in the tea.

To <u>tremble</u> *(v)* is to shake with quick, short movements, as from fear, excitement, weakness, or cold. The Roman soldiers began to <u>tremble</u> with fear when Jesus rose from the dead.

<u>Raw</u> *(adj)* is not cooked or prepared. Mother serves <u>raw</u> vegetables because they are very nutritious.

A <u>choir</u> *(n)* is a group of singers. Our church <u>choir</u> practiced the songs for the wedding Mass.

Puzzle

Choose a word from the word list to solve the crossword puzzle.

ACROSS

2 sweet-smelling herb
5 sharp at one end, hole at the other
8 building where monks live
10 habit of doing good

DOWN

1 flow of running water
3 to shake with quick, short movements
4 woman whose husband has died
6 group of singers
7 smooth, thick mixture
9 not cooked

Fill-in-the-Blanks

Fill in the blank with a word from the word list.

The monk used a _ and thread to mend his clothes.	1.
I like _ carrots better than cooked ones.	2.
Our pastor reminded us that charity to the poor is a _ .	3.
We grew basil, thyme, and fragrant _ in our herb garden.	4.
St. Elizabeth of Hungary was a _ who dedicated her life to helping the sick after her husband died.	5.
Jacinta taught our _ how to sing the *Gloria* for Mass next Sunday.	6.
The dentist said we could choose any flavor of tooth_ .	7.
The earthquake made our whole house _ .	8.
We brought bread and fruit to the monks at the _ .	9.
My toy boat began to float away down the _ , but our dog jumped in the water and caught it in his mouth!	10.

Word Usage

Replace the words in bold with the correct word from the word list.

We used **a sweet-smelling herb** in our homemade candy.	1.
Dad gave **uncooked** meat and bones to the hungry dogs.	2.
The Dominicans built their **home for monks** on Blue Mountain.	3.
The Christendom College **group of singers** sang for the bishop.	4.
My mom used a **small slender tool** to repair the altar cloths for the missionaries in Africa.	5.
The art teacher helped her students make a **sticky mixture** out of flour, water, and salt for their new project.	6.
Practicing **the habit of doing good and avoiding evil** is the first step to becoming a saint.	7.
Jesus told the leper to go wash himself in the **flow of running water.**	8.
The thought of meeting the Holy Father made her **shake** with excitement.	9.
The **woman who has not remarried since her husband died** prayed for her dead husband.	10.

Lesson 9: Word List

| clay | ruler | loaf | orchard | scoop |
| carpenter | wren | mayor | sacrifice | cashew |

Clay *(n)* **is a sticky kind of earth that hardens when it is baked.** Bricks and dishes are made from different kinds of **clay**.

A carpenter *(n)* **is a person who builds with wood.** A **carpenter** makes bookshelves, desks, parts of houses, and many other things.

A ruler *(n)* **is a straight strip of wood, metal, or plastic used for measuring and drawing lines.** I will measure this table with a **ruler**.

 **A wren** *(n)* **is a small, brown songbird, only a few inches long.** I saw that **wren** when he built his nest near my house.

A loaf *(n)* **is bread baked as one piece.** Aunt Julie brought a **loaf** of bread to dinner.

A mayor *(n)* **is the leader of a city or town.** The **mayor** promised the townspeople that the roads would be repaired.

An orchard *(n)* **is a piece of land on which fruit trees are grown.** We went to the **orchard** to pick a basket of fresh peaches.

A sacrifice *(n)* **is an act done to show sorrow for our sins, often involving giving something up.** What **sacrifice** did you make for Lent?

A scoop *(n)* **is a small kitchen utensil for removing a quantity of sugar, ice cream, or other food.** Mom used the **scoop** to serve the ice cream on top of the cherry pie.

A cashew *(n)* **is a nut that is shaped like the letter C, and is popular as a snack.** I ate only one **cashew** with a handful of peanuts from Mom's party tray.

Choose a word from the word list to solve the crossword puzzle.

ACROSS

1 nut
4 land with fruit trees
6 small brown songbird
7 leader of a city
9 sticky kind of earth
10 person who builds with wood

DOWN

2 kitchen utensil
3 act done to show sorrow for our sins
5 bread baked as one piece
8 used for measuring

Fill-in-the-Blanks

Fill in the blank with a word from the word list.

We helped our cousins pick fruit from their _ of apple, peach, and pear trees.	1.
St. Joseph worked as a _ to take care of Mary and Jesus.	2.
They forgot to bring a _ for serving the ice cream for the altar boys.	3.
We will bake a _ of pumpkin bread for the parish picnic.	4.
In her pottery class, my sister learned how to make a bowl out of _ .	5.
The _ is one nut you cannot buy in a shell!	6.
The Catholic _ led the town council in prayer at every meeting.	7.
A little _ and a robin sang by my windowsill on a bright spring morning.	8.
Using a _ , I measured four inches of snow that fell in our yard.	9.
The children of Fatima offered up their sufferings as a _ for the conversion of sinners.	10.

Word Usage

Circle the letter next to the sentence that uses the word correctly.

1. (a) Dad helped the **carpenter** build a bunk bed for the girls' room.
   (b) The **carpenter** made holes on a pole with its beak.

2. (a) Wheat, corn, and **orchard** grow in those farm fields.
   (b) The fruit from the **orchard** were ripe, juicy, and delicious!

3. (a) We need a **wren** and screws to put this table together.
   (b) I saw a **wren** and a pigeon out in our birdbath today.

4. (a) The girls decorated with pottery vases made of red **clay**.
   (b) Sprinkle some **clay** on the floors before you mop.

5. (a) You will need a **scoop** of sugar and four scoops of flour for this recipe.
   (b) The little **scoop** ate all of his breakfast.

6. (a) Use this **sacrifice** to make a knot at the end of the rosary beads.
   (b) The brothers gave up eating candy as a **sacrifice** for Lent.

7. (a) The **mayor** of the city suggested a plan to help the homeless.
   (b) That song is hard to play because it has so many chords and **mayor**.

8. (a) Jane used a hair **ruler** to make her hair curl.
   (b) We used the **ruler** to help us measure the size of the painting.

9. (a) The **cashew** bagged the food at the grocery store.
   (b) I tasted one salted **cashew,** and that was enough for me!

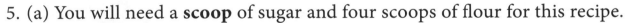

10. (a) The **loaf** made everyone laugh with his funny tricks.
    (b) We bought a **loaf** of freshly baked bread and buns at the bakery.

Lesson 10: Word List

panda	roast	marble	soar	elastic
confess	pave	praise	gallop	famous

A **panda** *(n)* is a small, white bear with black legs and black circles around its eyes. Our zoo obtained a six-month-old **panda** from the Cleveland Zoo.

To **confess** *(v)* is to admit having done something wrong. We Catholics **confess** our sins to God in the sacrament of Penance.

To **roast** *(v)* is to cook by heating in the oven. Mom will **roast** meat and potatoes for Sunday dinner.

To **pave** *(v)* is to cover with material (such as asphalt) to make a firm, level surface. If the town will **pave** our sidewalk, I will roller skate on it.

Marble *(n)* is a hard, usually white stone that can be polished; used to make altars, statues, staircases. Many religious statues are made with **marble**.

To **praise** *(v)* is to speak well of someone or something, or to worship. We **praise** God by attending Mass.

To **soar** *(v)* is to fly or rise high in the air. I saw the hawk **soar** over the trees by our house.

To **gallop** *(v)* is to run fast (usually refers to a horse). Paul Revere urged his horse to **gallop** so he could warn the citizens more quickly.

Elastic *(adj)* means able to be stretched and then returned to its own shape, such as rubber bands. Nina wrapped an **elastic** band around the cards to hold them together.

Famous *(adj)* means very well known. *St.* Thérèse became **famous** all over the world after people read about her.

Puzzle

Choose a word from the word list to solve the crossword puzzle.

ACROSS

3 able to be stretched
5 to cover a street to make it smooth
6 small bear with black circles around its eyes
7 hard, usually white stone
8 to rise high in the air
9 very well known

DOWN

1 to cook
2 to run
4 to admit having done something wrong
5 to speak well of someone

Fill in the blank with a word from the word list.

They will _ our long driveway so that I can ride my bike on it.	1.
My big brother knows how to _ a chicken.	2.
Tommy knew he should _ that he had broken the vase.	3.
The beautiful statue of Our Lady was made of smooth, white _ .	4.
The _ waistband of my skirt guarantees it will fit me just right.	5.
The *Little House* books became so _ , a television series was made about the family.	6.
At the zoo, we saw a koala from Australia and a _ from China.	7.
The students' good behavior caused the teacher to _ them.	8.
The small airplane began to _ high above the trees.	9.
The wild horse began to _ rapidly through the fields.	10.

Word Usage

Circle the letter next to the sentence that uses the word correctly.

1. (a) I was so tired on our walk that I started to **soar** down the street.
   (b) The eagle suddenly began to **soar** through the sky near the cliffs.

2. (a) Indians used sap from the Rubber Tree to make the first **elastic** rubber bands.
   (b) Monica pulled the **elastic** weeds out of the garden.

3. (a) Charlemagne was a **famous** Catholic king who helped spread the Catholic Faith in the Middle Ages.
   (b) Almost everyone has read some of Aesop's **famous.**

4. (a) The medicine started to **gallop** down Daniel's throat.
   (b) The Roman soldier's horse began to **gallop** toward the brave St. Tarcisius.

5. (a) The pope would **confess** his sins in confession every day.
   (b) Johnny is a very **confess** boy when he is happy.

6. (a) The statue of George Washington was made of rare Carrara **marble**.
   (b) The Seven Wonders of the World are a **marble.**

7. (a) A baby **panda** is pink when he is born and then turns black and white.
   (b) The **panda** dog licked me on my face with his big pink tongue.

8. (a) Use this pen to **pave** a straight line in your notebook.
   (b) The workers will **pave** a new walkway around the park.

9. (a) We will **roast** our turkey in the oven for Christmas.
   (b) After a long day at work, Tina likes to sit in her chair and **roast** her sore feet.

10. (a) The priest said we **praise** God twice when we sing the Mass prayers.
    (b) He who **praise** sings twice.

Lesson 11: Word List

acorn	harvest	caravan	grace	symbol
dough	eternal	wasp	tomahawk	scatter

An <u>acorn</u> (n) is the hard, brown nut of an oak tree. The squirrel cracked the <u>acorn</u> shell with its strong teeth.

<u>Dough</u> (n) is a flour mixture used to make bread or other baked goods. Veronica helped her grandma make the bread <u>dough</u>.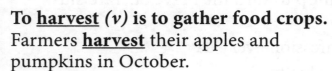

To <u>harvest</u> (v) is to gather food crops. Farmers <u>harvest</u> their apples and pumpkins in October.

 **<u>Eternal</u> (adj) means without beginning or end; everlasting.** God is the only Being Who is <u>eternal</u>.

A <u>caravan</u> (n) is a number of people traveling together. That <u>caravan</u> is traveling across the desert.

A <u>wasp</u> (n) is a kind of insect that has a slender body and a powerful sting. Unlike a bee, a <u>wasp</u> can sting more than once.

<u>Grace</u> (n) is God's divine life in our soul. The Angel Gabriel told Mary that she was full of <u>grace</u>.

A <u>tomahawk</u> (n) is a light axe, used by North American Indians as a weapon and a tool. The Indian fought bravely with just a knife and a <u>tomahawk</u>.

 **A <u>symbol</u> (n) is a sign that means, represents, or stands for something else.** The bald eagle is a <u>symbol</u> of the United States.

To <u>scatter</u> (v) is to throw in various directions. Dad began to <u>scatter</u> seeds in our garden.

Choose a word from the word list to solve the crossword puzzle.

ACROSS

2 light axe
5 God's divine life in our souls
6 to throw in various directions
7 to gather food crops
9 nut of an oak tree
10 flour mixture

DOWN

1 without beginning or end
3 insect with a powerful sting
4 people traveling together
8 sign that stands for something

Fill-in-the-Blanks

Fill in the blank with a word from the word list.

The busy squirrel chattered while looking for an _ to eat.	1.
Martha kneaded the _ for making bread while Mary sat and listened to Jesus.	2.
Baptism is the sacrament that gives our souls a new life of _ by which we become children of God.	3.
When the _ stung me, Mom put honey on the sting to lessen the pain.	4.
Jesus told the story about the farmer who went to _ seeds in different places.	5.
The farmers prayed to St. Isidore as they went to _ their crops.	6.
Our American flag is a _ of America.	7.
An Indian _ was found by the boys at an old fort.	8.
Joseph was sold by his brothers to a _ of Egyptian merchants passing through the desert.	9.
Jesus said, "Whoever keeps My commandments shall have _ life."	10.

Word Usage

Replace the words in bold with the correct word from the word list.

Marco Polo traveled in a **group of traveling people** across the desert into China.	1.
The doctor explained that the skull on the bottle is a **sign that means or stands** for danger or poison.	2.
We began to **throw in various directions** Easter eggs around the lawn for an Easter egg hunt.	3.
The hungry crow pecked at the **nut of an oak tree**, trying to eat it.	4.
When Adam sinned, he lost **God's divine life** in his soul.	5.
The **insect with a powerful sting** made its nest under our porch roof.	6.
The **light axe** lay on a mat in the Indian's teepee.	7.
Holy Communion is the food for our soul on the journey to our **everlasting** home in Heaven.	8.
The nuns prepared the **mixture to make bread** for the blessing of the bread on the feast of St. Joseph.	9.
Thomas worked hard helping his father **gather** the food crops for the family's winter supply.	10.

Lesson 12: Word List

| duet | lizard | award | sorrow | route |
| manhole | ripe | feast | leash | peddler |

A <u>duet</u> *(n)* is a song written for two instruments or voices, for two singers or players. My sister and I played "Danny Boy" as a <u>duet</u> on the piano.

A <u>manhole</u> *(n)* is a large opening in the street with a cover that can be taken off. That plumber went down into the <u>manhole</u> to make repairs on the sewers.

A <u>lizard</u> *(n)* is a small reptile somewhat like a snake, but usually having four legs. The <u>lizard</u> sticks out his throat when he is afraid or bothered.

<u>Ripe</u> *(adj)* means full-grown, ready to be gathered or eaten, as fruit. Nancy did not pick the cherries until they were <u>ripe</u>.

An <u>award</u> *(n)* is a prize, something given after a good performance. Amy was given an <u>award</u> for winning the race.

A <u>feast</u> *(n)* is a celebration including a meal prepared for a special event. Jesus worked His first miracle during the wedding <u>feast</u> at Cana.

<u>Sorrow</u> *(n)* is grief, sadness, or regret. <u>Sorrow</u> for sin is necessary for a good confession.

A <u>leash</u> *(n)* is a strap or rope for controlling an animal. George uses a <u>leash</u> when he takes his puppy for walks.

A <u>route</u> *(n)* is a way to go; a road. The mailman's <u>route</u> takes him all the way around town.

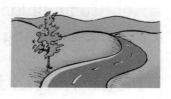

A <u>peddler</u> *(n)* is a person who travels about selling things which he carries in a pack or cart. The <u>peddler</u> tried to sell me some pots and pans.

Puzzle

Choose a word from the word list to solve the crossword puzzle.

ACROSS

1 four-legged reptile
4 celebration including a meal
7 grief, sadness
9 strap for holding an animal
10 person who travels about selling things

DOWN

2 song written for two
3 large opening in the street with a cover
5 something given after a good performance
6 way to go
8 full-grown

Fill-in-the-Blanks

Fill in the blank with a word from the word list.

The Three Wise Men were warned by an angel not to go back to King Herod, but to take another _ back to their own country.	1.
A _ peach is soft and juicy.	2.
That _ is a local farmer who is selling his vegetables and fruits from the back of his truck.	3.
My brother wrote a violin _ for him and me to play at the concert.	4.
My pet _ is only four inches long, but some in the zoo are several feet long.	5.
Mother Teresa of Calcutta was given an _ because of her charity for those in need.	6.
Mom has planned a large _ for our family to celebrate Easter.	7.
Peter's heart became filled with _ because he regretted his lie that he did not know Jesus.	8.
When my dog wants to go out for his walk, he brings his collar and _ to me.	9.
The sewer worker climbed down into a _ in the street.	10.

Word Usage

Circle the letter next to the sentence that uses the word correctly.

1. (a) Children slid down the slides and crawled through the **lizard** in the park.
   (b) The Anole **lizard**, common in Florida, can change its color from green to brown.

2. (a) Smokey's long **leash** was tangled in the bushes.
   (b) A baby **leash** will crawl out of its eggs when it hatches.

3. (a) After Jesus' death, the apostles spent three days in **sorrow** in the Upper Room.
   (b) Rosie made **sorrow** dough bread for tomorrow's breakfast.

4. (a) The **route** of the cucumber plant needs plenty of water to grow big and healthy.
   (b) "Drive twenty miles north on **Route** 522 to get to Winchester."

5. (a) The hunters made a **manhole** to trap the wild animals.
   (b) There was smoke coming out of the **manhole** in the street.

6. (a) Elizabeth and Jacinta played a flute and piano **duet**.
   (b) Roger and George played a **duet** with their basketball.

7. (a) Jimmy, the **peddler**, comes by each month to sell his tools.
   (b) The **peddler** at the bike shop fixed our bicycle's pedal that was broken.

8. (a) At the wedding **feast** of Cana, Jesus turned water into wine.
   (b) The king of Bavaria awarded the young knight for his **feast** of bravery.

9. (a) Let's make a banana **ripe** for dessert.
   (b) Bartholomew picked the **ripe**, red strawberries from the garden.

10. (a) Rita won the first place **award** at the horse show.
    (b) Fill in the blank with an **award**.

Lesson 13: Word List

feather	fawn	ink	ramble	breeze
consecrate	treasure	angle	barrel	yard

A <u>feather</u> *(n)* is a part of a bird that grows out from its skin, that keeps it warm, and makes it able to fly. As the bird flew away, a single red <u>feather</u> floated to the ground.

To <u>consecrate</u> *(v)* is to set apart as sacred, to make holy; dedicate. The bishop came to the new church to <u>consecrate</u> it in time for the Easter Mass.

A <u>fawn</u> *(n)* is a baby deer less than one year old. *Bambi* is the story of a <u>fawn</u> who learns to live on his own.

<u>Treasure</u> *(n)* is something valuable that is stored up. The huge chest in the palace was full of gold and other <u>treasure</u>.

<u>Ink</u> *(n)* is liquid used for writing or printing. Before pens were made, people used quills or feathers dipped in a jar of <u>ink</u> to write.

An <u>angle</u> *(n)* is the shape made by two straight lines that connect. The measure of one <u>angle</u> in a square is equal to the other angles.

To <u>ramble</u> *(v)* is to wander in speaking, writing, or walking. The speaker started to <u>ramble</u> on about the price of eggs.

A <u>barrel</u> *(n)* is a container with a round, flat top and bottom, and slightly curved sides; usually made of boards held together by metal hoops. We used a large <u>barrel</u> to ship the molasses.

A <u>breeze</u> *(n)* is a stirring of air or a light wind. The kite flew into the air once the brisk <u>breeze</u> began to blow.

A <u>yard</u> *(n) is a* measure of length three feet long. Dad said he would help my brother build a desk one <u>yard</u> wide.

Puzzle

Choose a word from the word list to solve the crossword puzzle.

ACROSS

3 three feet
4 a baby deer
5 makes a bird able to fly
6 to wander in speaking
8 something valuable
10 shape made by two straight lines that connect

DOWN

1 a light wind
2 to set apart as sacred
7 a round container with a flat top
9 liquid used for writing

Fill-in-the-Blanks

Fill in the blank with a word from the word list.

When Jesus ordered the storm to stop, it became a gentle _.	1.
Dad found a huge _ to store his special tools.	2.
Any _ in a square is the same size and shape as the other three.	3.
Mother measured a _ of pink silk to make a special Easter hat.	4.
The bishop will _ the hands of the newly-ordained priests.	5.
Jesus taught that our real _ is in Heaven, not in gold or silver.	6.
An octopus, when scared, squirts out a dark liquid called _ , like the liquid in a pen!	7.
I watched the little _ wobble on its thin legs as it learned to walk.	8.
Louis started to _ when telling his very long story.	9.
Just as every _ on a bird helps it to fly in the sky, so every prayer helps us to grow closer to God.	10.

Word Usage

Circle the letter next to the sentence that uses the word correctly.

1. (a) I ran around on the sandy beach in my **barrel** feet.
   (b) Johnny scooped the flour from the **barrel** to make pizza dough.

2. (a) "Don't let the dogs **ramble** the garden, or they'll smash the little plants!"
   (b) "Don't **ramble**, Little Red Riding Hood, but go straight to Grandmother's house."

3. (a) It is much easier to write with a pen than with a quill and a bottle of **ink**.
   (b) A chain is only as strong as its weakest **ink**.

4. (a) Each **feather** on a duck is oily to keep the duck warm.
   (b) We picked a **feather** from the tree for a collection.

5. (a) "How fast can you play a **treasure** on the piano?"
   (b) We must share the **treasure** of our Catholic Faith with other people.

6. (a) It had been so hot and sticky that the **breeze** felt refreshing.
   (b) The choir director told us to take a deep **breeze** before we begin our song.

7. (a) Before lighting the candles, Father read a **consecrate** and we sang hymns.
   (b) The Indian wanted to **consecrate** herself to God at the Indian mission.

8. (a) A **fawn** stays hidden in the grass until it is strong enough to walk.
   (b) The new game was so **fawn** that we played it all evening.

9. (a) Dad said that when building anything, each **angle** must be carefully measured.
   (b) The old doll would **angle** over if you tried to stand her up.

10. (a) We were as close as one **yard** from the incorrupt body of
    St. Vincent.
    (b) "I will teach you to knit if you will teach me to **yard**."

Lesson 14: Word List

island	apron	shiver	adult	saddle
orphan	lantern	dozen	apostle	chalice

An <u>island</u> *(n)* is a piece of land that is surrounded by water. To reach an <u>island</u>, you must sail on a boat, or fly by plane.

An <u>orphan</u> *(n)* is a child whose parents have died. After being taken care of by foster parents, the <u>orphan</u> joined the seminary and became a priest.

An <u>apron</u> *(n)* is a material worn on top of a person's clothes to protect them. The waitress' name was stitched on her <u>apron</u>.

A <u>lantern</u> *(n)* is a glass case to protect a light from wind or rain. Paul Revere hung a <u>lantern</u> in the Old North Church in Boston.

To <u>shiver</u> *(v)* is to shake with cold or fear. When the children went outside for sledding, they began to <u>shiver</u> from the cold.

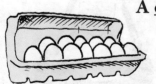

A <u>dozen</u> *(n)* is a group of twelve. Eggs are usually sold by the <u>dozen</u>.

An <u>adult</u> *(n)* is a person or animal that is fully grown or mature. Though my aunt is an <u>adult</u>, she loves to play with the children.

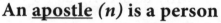

An <u>apostle</u> *(n)* is a person chosen by Christ to carry out His mission of spreading the Gospel. St. Peter, the <u>apostle</u>, was chosen by Jesus to be the first head of the Church.

A <u>saddle</u> *(n)* is a leather seat for a rider on a horse's back. Dad gave her a golden leather <u>saddle</u> to use while riding her new pony.

A <u>chalice</u> *(n)* is a vessel like a cup that will hold the Precious Blood of Jesus after a priest consecrates it during the Mass. The <u>chalice</u> that Father Bart used was made of gold and silver.

Puzzle

Choose a word from the word list to solve the crossword puzzle.

ACROSS

1 to shake with cold

5 person chosen by Christ to spread the Gospel

7 seat for a rider on a horse's back

9 something worn to protect clothes

10 vessel that holds the Blood of Jesus

DOWN

2 land surrounded by water

3 case to protect a light from wind

4 child whose parents have died

6 group of twelve

8 fully grown person

Fill-in-the-Blanks

Fill in the blank with a word from the word list.

Mom wears an _ when she makes cookies so she will not get flour on her clothes.	1.
Though my uncle was an _ , the bishop confirmed him with the children's class.	2.
St. John was the only _ who stood at the foot of the Cross with the Blessed Mother.	3.
Hawaii is a large _ , known for its beautiful beaches, scuba diving, and ocean cruises.	4.
Before electricity, one had to use a _ to see at night.	5.
St. John Bosco made a home for the poor _ and taught him to pray, work, learn, and play.	6.
Since Cathy had the flu, it made her _ with cold, even on a warm, sunny day.	7.
The priest carefully wiped the gold _ after Communion.	8.
Grandma brought some oranges; there were a _ , one for each of her twelve grandchildren.	9.
Robin Hood brushed his horse, put on the _ , and galloped through Sherwood Forest.	10.

Word Usage

Replace the words in bold with the correct word from the word list.

Because of the sale, we were able to buy 24 doughnuts for the price of a **group of twelve**.	1. _____
I like the English **leather horse seat for riders** because it is less bulky than the Western.	2. _____
A **vessel consecrated to hold the Precious Blood of Jesus** must be silver or gold, at least on the inside.	3. _____
Christopher Columbus discovered Cuba, a beautiful, tropical **piece of land surrounded by water,** ninety miles south of Florida.	4. _____
The boy was safely guided to a chapel in the woods by an angel with a **glass case to protect the light from wind or rain.**	5. _____
St. James was the first **person chosen by Christ to carry out His mission** to be martyred.	6. _____
The little **child whose parents have died** knelt in the church and asked Jesus and Mary to become his heavenly parents.	7. _____
The **person fully grown** sat down and talked while the children played.	8. _____
Each of the girls put on an **material worn on top of the clothes to protect them** and helped Anna make cherry pies.	9. _____
When you **shake with cold**, your muscles are tightening and loosening, trying to warm you up.	10. _____

Lesson 15: Word List

character	harbor	cradle	angel	create
mercy	soak	ladle	reptile	ostrich

A <u>character</u> (*n*) is a person or animal in a story or play. Clara is the main <u>character</u> in *The Nutcracker*.

<u>Mercy</u> (*n*) is true kindness and forgiveness. Our Lord, in His <u>mercy</u>, died for our sins on the Cross.

A <u>harbor</u> (*n*) is a place of shelter where boats are kept. Fishermen tie their boats in the <u>harbor</u> at night.

To <u>soak</u> (*v*) is to put something in liquid for a long time. Mom said to <u>soak</u> the burned pan overnight.

A <u>cradle</u> (*n*) is a baby's bed on rockers. Since Mary had no <u>cradle</u>, she placed Baby Jesus in a manger.

A <u>ladle</u> (*n*) is a deep, cup-shaped spoon with a long handle, for scooping out liquids. Nina used the new <u>ladle</u> to serve her vegetable soup.

An <u>angel</u> (*n*) is a pure spirit, a being without a body, who lives in Heaven. St. Gabriel was the <u>angel</u> who appeared to Mary.

A <u>reptile</u> (*n*) is a cold-blooded animal that creeps or crawls. Grandpa said that my pet turtle is a <u>reptile</u> which likes to be in water as well as on land.

To <u>create</u> (*v*) is to make something out of nothing, or to invent something. The sculptor will <u>create</u> a beautiful statue out of the marble stone.

An <u>ostrich</u> (*n*) is a large, African bird that can run very fast, but cannot fly. An <u>ostrich</u> will lie flat on the ground to hide from an enemy.

Puzzle

Choose a word from the word list to solve the crossword puzzle.

ACROSS

2 place where boats are kept
6 true forgiveness
8 to make something out of nothing
9 baby's bed on rockers
10 deep cup-shaped spoon

DOWN

1 person in a story
3 pure spirit without a body
4 large, African bird that can run very fast
5 cold-blooded animal that crawls
7 to put something in liquid

Fill-in-the-Blanks

Fill in the blank with a word from the word list.

My favorite _ in *The Lion, the Witch, and the Wardrobe* is Lucy.	1.
I have seen that _ lie in the sun to warm up.	2.
God sent the _ Raphael to obtain the medicine to help old Tobit.	3.
Jessica rocked her new baby in his _ and sang him to sleep.	4.
The large _ from Africa ran at an amazing speed from the lion.	5.
Three o'clock is called The Hour of Divine _ because it is the hour in which Our Lord died on the Cross for our sins.	6.
Alexander Graham Bell wanted to _ an invention for people to talk to each other from far away.	7.
In 1941, the Japanese bombed some U.S. battleships that were anchored in a _ in Hawaii.	8.
Mother said she needs to _ our stained shirts in a tub of soapy water.	9.
The nuns used a large _ to serve the soup to the hungry orphans.	10.

Word Usage

Circle the letter next to the sentence that uses the word correctly.

1. (a) The boys climbed up the **ladle** to their treehouse.
   (b) Please put the **ladle** in the serving bowl on the table.

2. (a) Wash the dishes with **soak** and water.
   (b) A sudden summer rain can **soak** a person in seconds.

3. (a) Christopher Columbus' ships, the Niña, the Pinta, and the Santa Maria, were in the **harbor**, ready for their voyage.
   (b) I hammered the nail **harbor**, but that only bent the nail.

4. (a) Glenn Miller wanted to **create** a new sound with his band.
   (b) Dad will **create** the fish scales before we fry them.

5. (a) The **mercy** parade is held in New York.
   (b) For the sake of His sorrowful Passion, have **mercy** on us and on the whole world.

6. (a) My mother's new Easter hat contains several beautiful feathers from an **ostrich**.
   (b) At the park, we were surprised to see an **ostrich** fly high over our heads.

7. (a) My dad made a new **cradle** when baby Thomas was born.
   (b) Mary's mother made her a white dress and a **cradle** to wear.

8. (a) Each angel must be carefully measured.
   (b) The guardian angel of Portugal appeared to Lucia, Francisco, and Jacinta.

9. (a) That **reptile** lives in the water and lays eggs.
   (b) The workers laid the new **reptile** floor in the kitchen.

10. (a) A **character** comes to our house every year to tune our piano.
    (b) Miss Kelly chose who would play each **character** in the play.

Lesson 16: Word List

glossary	burglar	dairy	chorus	band
warehouse	procession	chimpanzee	miracle	whiskers

A **glossary** *(n)* **is a list of words found in the back of a book, with definitions for each word.** My science book has a **glossary** so I can find the meaning of words.

A **warehouse** *(n)* **is a large building used to store things that will be sold.** The Seton **warehouse** was full of new books ready to be sent out to the students.

A **burglar** *(n)* **is a person who breaks into a building intending to steal something.** The police caught the **burglar** as he climbed out the window of the house.

A **procession** *(n)* **is a group of people moving forward in an orderly way.** The Blessed Sacrament is carried by the priest in a Corpus Christi **procession**.

Dairy *(adj)* **means relating to or producing milk, butter, cheese, or yogurt.** A **dairy** farm is where cows are kept to give milk.

A **chimpanzee** *(n)* **is a large, monkey-like animal with no tail that lives in the jungles of Africa.** The **chimpanzee** was swinging from branch to branch.

A **chorus** *(n)* **is a group of singers; something sung together by a group of people.** All of the people in the church sang the "Great Amen" **chorus**.

A **miracle** *(n)* **is something wonderful that can be done only by the power of God.** It was a **miracle** that he was not hurt in the car accident.

A **band** *(n)* **is a group of people working together.** The **band** of musicians sponsored a concert to raise money for the poor.

Whiskers *(n)* **are hairs growing from the chin or the sides of the face.** A cat's white **whiskers** are stiff and straight.

Puzzle

Choose a word from the word list to solve the crossword puzzle.

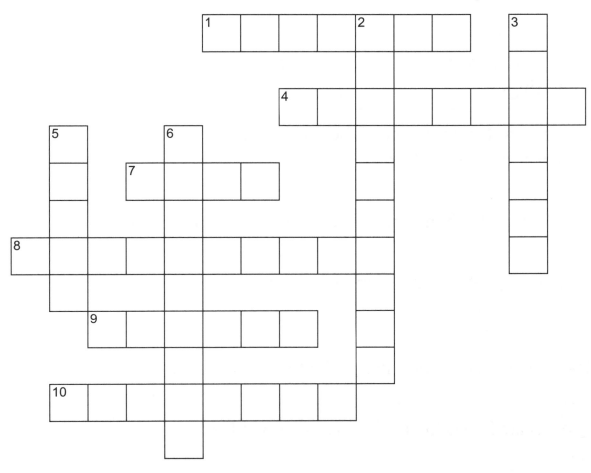

ACROSS

1 something done by the power of God
4 hair growing from the chin or the sides of the face
7 group of people working together
8 group moving in an orderly way
9 something sung together by a group of people
10 list of words with definitions

DOWN

2 large monkey-like animal with no tail that lives in Africa
3 person who breaks into a building intending to steal
5 producing milk
6 large building used to store things that will be sold

Fill-in-the-Blanks

Fill in the blank with a word from the word list.

The _ broke into the jewelry store and stole all the diamond rings.	1.
The flower girls tossed rose petals before the Blessed Sacrament at the Corpus Christi _ .	2.
Our family buys fresh milk and cheese from the _ farm.	3.
I looked in the _ of my catechism to find out what "apostolic" means.	4.
Jessica's brother plays drums in a _ with three other men.	5.
The _ on a cat's face help him feel his way around in the dark.	6.
The tire factory stored its tires in a huge _ before shipping them.	7.
Our church _ sang several songs for our parish Christmas party.	8.
A _ happens at every holy Mass when the bread and wine become the Body and Blood of Jesus.	9.
Our zoo has gorillas, orangutans, and a _ that was brought from the jungles of Africa.	10.

Word Usage

Circle the letter next to the sentence that used the word correctly.

1. (a) Our kitten sniffed at a candle and burned the tips of his **whiskers**.
   (b) Mother told us to **whisker** during Mass.

2. (a) The colonists formed a **band** of riflemen to fight the English.
   (b) The town **band** the playing of loud music after eight o'clock.

3. (a) Do you know about the **miracle** that happened at Fatima?
   (b) Barbara's wedding dress was so beautiful and looked **miracle** on her.

4. (a) The girls learned to make butter at their aunt's **dairy** store.
   (b) Our **dairy** breakfast is scrambled eggs and bacon.

5. (a) A **chorus** of angels' voices sang, "Glory to God in the highest!"
   (b) The early Americans made **chorus** for their meals.

6. (a) We will fill these boxes with new books and store them in the **warehouse**.
   (b) She grew up in a **warehouse** that had four bedrooms and two bathrooms.

7. (a) A **procession** of cars moved toward the cemetery on All Souls' Day.
   (b) Make sure all the children **procession** home after school.

8. (a) Don't **glossary** over the facts.
   (b) This **glossary** has over a hundred words in it.

9. (a) The **chimpanzee** chattered and swung on the tall branches.
   (b) A squirrel and its **chimpanzee** ate nuts from our hands.

10. (a) The **burglar** broke into the bank last weekend.
    (b) The **burglar** rushed to the home to put out the fire.

Lesson 17: Word List

| echo | bait | season | crack | tithe |
| bulldozer | soul | skim | universe | salmon |

An **echo** *(n)* is the repeating of a sound caused by sound waves bouncing back. Tommy heard an **echo** in the cave.

A **bulldozer** *(n)* is a tractor with a heavy blade in front to clear away earth and rocks. The men used a **bulldozer** to clear the land where our house will be built.

Bait *(n)* is food used to attract and catch fish or other animals. It was a miracle when St. Peter caught hundreds of fish but used no **bait**.

The **soul** *(n)* is the spiritual part of a person which lives forever. We should pray for the **soul** of any family member who has died.

A **season** *(n)* is a certain time of the year that is marked by something special. Spring is such a beautiful **season**.

To **skim** *(v)* is to remove from the top. The cook will **skim** the grease from the top of the gravy.

To **crack** (v) is to break, split, or snap apart. Mom likes to **crack** open the eggs on the side of the frying pan.

The **universe** *(n)* is all of creation around us, including the planet Earth, stars, and all of outer space. God created the whole **universe**.

To **tithe** *(v)* is to give one-tenth part of income to support a church. In order for our church to pay its bills on time, the members were all asked to **tithe** each week.

A **salmon** *(n)* is a large fish with silvery scales and yellowish-pink skin. Canned **salmon** is good to eat, but not as good as fresh salmon.

Puzzle

Choose a word from the word list to solve the crossword puzzle.

ACROSS

2 spiritual part of a person
4 to remove from the top
5 certain time of the year
8 to give ten percent
9 to break apart
10 large fish with yellowish-pink skin

DOWN

1 tractor with a heavy blade in front
3 all of creation around us
6 food used to attract animals
7 repeating of a sound

Fill-in-the-Blanks

Fill in the blank with a word from the word list.

My favorite time of year is the Christmas _ .	1.
You can hear an _ if you shout in the Grand Canyon.	2.
Mother will _ the cream from the top of the milk and whip it into butter.	3.
Astronomers tell us there are millions of stars in the _ .	4.
The Blessed Mother was assumed body and _ into Heaven after she died.	5.
A _ will clear the land so that we can begin building a new church.	6.
Cheese is good _ not only for catching mice, but also for catching fish!	7.
Dad had to use a heavy knife to _ open the huge watermelon!	8.
My parents _ to support the work of the Church.	9.
_ is a very common fish in Alaska.	10.

Word Usage

Replace the words in bold with the correct word from the word list.

The Blessed Mother is the queen of the **whole of creation around us.**	1.
The boys attached the **food used to attract animals** on their hooks before the fishing trip.	2.
Dan tried to **scrape off** the growth from the top of the pond.	3.
I used a hammer to **break** the shells of the walnuts.	4.
We heard a **repeating of sounds** in the empty room.	5.
Our pastor urged the congregation to **give a tenth of one's earnings** each week.	6.
God made my **source of life that will live forever** in His own image and likeness.	7.
During the **certain time of year** of fall, we help Grandma pick apples to make apple sauce.	8.
One of Grandfather's favorite meals on Friday is smoked **silver-scaled and pink-skinned fish.**	9.
With a **tractor with a heavy blade**, my uncle cleared a path in the woods.	10.

Lesson 18: Word List

respect	marry	increase	habit	divine
beaver	cottage	chest	frustrated	stilts

Respect (n) is a show of great admiration and reverence. St. Tarcisius had such a deep **respect** for the Eucharist that he gave his life to protect It.

A beaver (n) is an animal with soft brown fur, sharp front teeth, and a flat tail. A **beaver** likes to live near streams and build dams.

To marry (v) is to join as husband and wife. Father Carr will **marry** the couple at St. Eugene's Church.

A cottage (n) is a small house, often used as a vacation home. Little Red Riding Hood visited her grandmother's **cottage**.

To increase (v) is to become bigger or greater in amount. The bishop wants to **increase** the number of priests in the diocese.

The chest (n) is the upper part of the human body where the heart and lungs are located. Mom told little Billy not to go into the water above his **chest**.

A habit (n) is a custom or practice that a person gets used to doing. Our family has a good **habit** of praying the Rosary every evening after dinner.

Frustrated (adj) is being disappointed, not able to accomplish a desire to do something. Daniel was **frustrated** because the wind kept blowing back the leaves he had raked.

Divine (adj) is something of God, to God, or for God; something sacred or holy. **Divine** worship is the worship given to God.

Stilts (n) are two long poles with supports for the feet; used for walking. **Stilts** are sometimes used by clowns to entertain people.

Puzzle

Choose a word from the word list to solve the crossword puzzle.

ACROSS

1 show of great admiration
3 disappointed not to accomplish something
6 custom or practice that a person gets used to doing
8 animal with soft brown fur and sharp front teeth
9 upper part of the body between the stomach and the neck
10 to become bigger or greater

DOWN

2 small house
4 two long poles with supports for the feet
5 to join as husband and wife
7 something sacred that is about God

Fill-in-the-Blanks

Fill in the blank with a word from the word list.

When Tim had the measles, the rash was on his face and _.	1. _____
The saints are holy, but only God is _.	2. _____
After many years, Monica finally agreed to _ Paul and become his wife.	3. _____
Snow White and Rose Red lived in a small _ in the woods.	4. _____
It is a good _ to brush your teeth after every meal.	5. _____
I have great _ for the work of the missionaries.	6. _____
I found it difficult to learn to balance myself on those _.	7. _____
My parents decided to _ the amount of money they give to the poor.	8. _____
The baseball player was _ because his injury stopped him from playing.	9. _____
A _ loves to swim in streams and use his sharp front teeth to shape logs and build dams.	10. _____

Word Usage

Circle the letter next to the sentence that uses the word correctly.

1. (a) Everyone had a very **marry** Christmas.
   (b) The Church advises a couple wait six months before they **marry**.

2. (a) The Leaning Tower of Pisa **stilts** on one side high above the city.
   (b) On his **stilts,** the clown did many tricks to make people laugh.

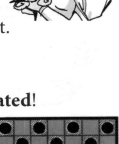

3. (a) Practicing a good **habit** now will help us be better persons later.
   (b) He wore a **habit** for playing out in the rain so he wouldn't get wet.

4. (a) I was so **frustrated** to solve the math problem at last!
   (b) I could not solve the difficult math problem and was very **frustrated**!

5. (a) Ken beat Stephen at **chest** and checkers two times in a row.
   (b) The marine in uniform wore several medals on his **chest**.

6. (a) A popular novena is the **Divine** Mercy Novena.
   (b) Today we are going to learn to **divine** and multiply in Math.

7. (a) The **cottage** was melting in the sun because no one covered it.
   (b) Dad rented a **cottage** on the mountain for our skiing vacation.

8. (a) We must try to **increase** devotion to the Sacred Heart.
   (b) My mother uses an iron to put an **increase** in my brother's shirt.

9. (a) Children must show **respect** to their parents at all times.
   (b) There was a **respect** on my glasses.

10. (a) Those animals will **beaver** together in their dens to stay warm.
    (b) The fur of a **beaver** is soft and warm and is used to make coats and caps.

Lesson 19: Word List

relic	balcony	serpent	steam	shrine
hoof	float	ankle	code	attach

A <u>relic</u> *(n)* is something belonging to a saint that is kept as a reminder of his holiness. A <u>relic</u> of a saint is kept in the altar of every Catholic church.

A <u>hoof</u> *(n)* is the hard covering on the foot of a horse, cow, sheep, pig, and other animals. The horse has a stone stuck in his <u>hoof</u>.

A <u>balcony</u> *(n)* is a platform, usually with a railing, on the outside of a building. I was nervous when I looked over the <u>balcony</u> at the ground below.

To <u>float</u> *(v)* is to rest on the surface of a liquid or in the air without sinking. The toddler liked to <u>float</u> his toy boat in the bathtub.

A <u>serpent</u> *(n)* is a large snake. The boa constrictor is a <u>serpent</u> that can grow to be thirteen feet long.

The <u>ankle</u> *(n)* is the joint or place where the foot joins the leg. The water in the pond was only as high as my <u>ankle</u>.

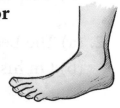

<u>Steam</u> *(n)* is water that has been turned into a white mist by being heated. Nan looked at the <u>steam</u> coming from her cassarole in the oven.

A <u>code</u> *(n)* is a special way of writing or sending messages to keep them short or secret. Sometimes soldiers use a <u>code</u> to send secret messages.

A <u>shrine</u> *(n)* is a sacred place where holy things are kept, such as relics of a saint. We visited the <u>shrine</u> of St. Elizabeth Ann Seton in Maryland.

To <u>attach</u> *(v)* is to fasten or join two things together. My brother will <u>attach</u> a rope to his sled.

Puzzle

Choose a word from the word list to solve the crossword puzzle.

ACROSS

5 a sacred place where holy things are kept

6 to rest on the surface of a liquid

8 a platform on a building that sticks out in the open air

9 a way to keep messages secret

10 a hard covering on the foot of some animals

DOWN

1 place where the foot joins the leg

2 a large snake

3 something that belonged to a saint

4 to fasten or join

7 water that has become a white mist

Fill-in-the-Blanks

Fill in the blank with a word from the word list.

The devil in the form of a _ tempted Eve to eat the fruit of the tree in the Garden of Eden.	1.
Sometimes brothers and sisters make up their own _ to send each other private messages.	2.
Mom showed me how to _ the pictures in my scrapbook.	3.
As the _ of St. Blaise touched the sick man's throat, he was instantly cured.	4.
The cowboy could see that there was a crack in the horse's _.	5.
Pete twisted his _ last summer when he was playing football.	6.
Mother Angelica built a _ devoted to the Blessed Sacrament.	7.
The first boat engine ran on _ ; water heated by burning firewood was used to make the boat move.	8.
Standing on the _ of the tall building, we watched the parade pass by on the street below.	9.
Susie showed her little sister how to _ in the swimming pool.	10.

Word Usage

Circle the letter next to the sentence that uses the word correctly.

1. (a) Timothy stacked old crates in the warehouse and put a **relic** on top to hold them.
   (b) St. Helen, the mother of Emperor Constantine, found the **relic** of the Holy Cross.

2. (a) "Don't forget to **attach** the license plate on the new car," called out the salesman.
   (b) The commander ordered his soldiers to **attach**.

3. (a) My **ankle** became swollen after I went ice skating.
   (b) I put gloves on my **ankle** so I could weed the garden.

4. (a) The statue of the Blessed Mother shows her crushing the **serpent** under her feet.
   (b) The priest called for everyone to **serpent** of their sins.

5. (a) The duck has an orange **hoof** that helps him swim in the water.
   (b) Robert hammered the iron horseshoe on the **hoof** of Corky, the horse.

6. (a) Many people visit St. John Vianney's **shrine** in Ars, France.
   (b) Our great-grandfather built the **shrine** for the church steeple's top.

7. (a) Patty put on her **float** before going on the long walk to town
      with Daddy.
   (b) The helium balloon began to **float** away from the little boy.

8. (a) Philip likes to help Dad fill the car's tank with **steam** at the gas station.
   (b) The **steam** rose from our hot chocolate as we sipped it by the fireplace.

9. (a) The spy sat at his radio and began to send out his message in secret **code**.
   (b) My sister wore her new blue **code** on the first day of winter.

10. (a) It was fun to slide down the **balcony** in the park.
    (b) The fire fighters climbed up the ladder to reach the high **balcony** of the house.

Lesson 20: Word List

tongs	vestments	wisp	whale	moat
ornament	harmony	margin	hose	sacristy

A pair of <u>tongs</u> (*n*) is a tool that is used for lifting and holding things. Use the <u>tongs</u> to pick up the hot ears of corn from the pan.

An <u>ornament</u> (*n*) is a decoration or anything pretty that is used to add beauty. Dad hung the lights, and then I hung my special <u>ornament</u> on the Christmas tree.

<u>Vestments</u> (*n*) are robes worn by the priest and altar servers during the Mass. Do you know when the priest wears purple <u>vestments</u> for Mass?

<u>Harmony</u> (*n*) is the playing or singing of musical notes together for a blending of sounds. The choir sang in perfect <u>harmony</u> for the Easter Mass.

A <u>wisp</u> (*n*) is a thin bunch of something such as hair, smoke, or clouds. A thin <u>wisp</u> of smoke curled out of the chimney.

The <u>margin</u> (*n*) is the blank space around a page, or an edge or border around something. Mom wrote one of her favorite recipes in the <u>margin</u> of her cookbook.

A <u>whale</u> (*n*) is a huge sea animal. A baby <u>whale</u> is the size of an elephant.

A <u>hose</u> (*n*) is a tube made of rubber or something that can bend, which is used to carry liquids. Kristy watered her flowers with her green garden <u>hose</u>.

A <u>moat</u> (*n*) is a deep, wide ditch dug around a castle and filled with water for protection against enemies. People could enter a castle across a drawbridge over a <u>moat</u>.

A <u>sacristy</u> (*n*) is a small room near the altar where all the things used for holy Mass are kept. Father Francis dressed for Mass in the <u>sacristy</u>.

Puzzle

Choose a word from the word list to solve the crossword puzzle.

ACROSS

5 small room in a church near the altar

7 empty space around a page

8 tube used to carry liquids

10 tool used for lifting and holding things

DOWN

1 small bunch of something such as hair

2 blending of musical notes

3 special robes worn by a priest during Mass

4 something pretty used to decorate

6 huge sea animal

9 deep ditch with water around a castle

Fill in the blank with a word from the word list.

Sally tucked a _ of hair back under her winter cap.	1.
The music teacher was surprised that the three sisters could sing in perfect _.	2.
Dad used a pair of _ to turn over the hamburgers on the grill.	3.
The altar boys arrived early in the _ to dress for Mass.	4.
A _ cannot breathe under water; it must come to the surface of the sea to breathe.	5.
Rose made a large, beautifully decorated Easter egg as an _ for the dinner table on Easter Sunday.	6.
The castle tower rang out an alarm, and the drawbridge over the _ was lifted to prevent enemies from entering!	7.
The firemen saved the burning house by spraying the flames with water from a long _.	8.
The priests wear red _ on the feasts of the martyrs to remind us they shed their blood for the Faith.	9.
The monk painted a beautiful border on the _ of the page he was copying.	10.

Word Usage

Replace the words in bold with the correct word from the word list.

The king's treasure chest contained an **object used to add beauty** that could be used to decorate a Christmas tree.	1.
The altar boys prepared for Benediction in the **room where all the things used for holy Mass are kept.**	2.
There were secret tunnels under the castle's **wide ditch filled with water**, so that if danger came, the people could escape.	3.
Lisa put a sticky note on the **empty space around a page** of her book to mark the important page.	4.
The blue **sea animal** can grow up to one hundred feet long!	5.
A **small puff** of smoke from the twigs showed that Tom had finally started the fire.	6.
Robes worn by a priest during the Mass are somewhat similar to the usual clothes that men wore in Roman times.	7.
We like to hear the barbershop quartet sing in **a blending of musical notes**.	8.
We use the **tube made of rubber** for watering the garden and washing the car.	9.
He lifted and stirred the hot coals with **the tool used for lifting and holding things** to get the fire started.	10.

Lesson 21: Word List

| parachute | picnic | incense | hive | volcano |
| flag | banjo | dentist | disappear | tangle |

A <u>parachute</u> *(n)* is a huge, umbrella-shaped cloth with strings from which a person can hang while dropping safely from an airplane to the ground. The soldier quickly opened his <u>parachute</u> as he was dropped into enemy territory!

A <u>flag</u> *(n)* is a piece of cloth with special colors or patterns, usually to represent a nation or an organization. We have a yellow and white Vatican <u>flag</u> in our church.

A <u>picnic</u> *(n)* is a meal made to be eaten outdoors. Betty loves to have a <u>picnic</u>, but I like to eat inside.

A <u>banjo</u> *(n)* is a musical instrument with a round body, a long neck, and five strings, much like a guitar. Alex played a lively tune on the <u>banjo</u>.

<u>Incense</u> *(n)* is a sand-like material that gives off a sweet smell when burned. The use of <u>incense</u> at church is a sign of honor and worship.

A <u>dentist</u> *(n)* is a person whose job is to fill, clean, or repair teeth. The <u>dentist</u> checked my teeth and told me to make a habit of brushing them twice a day.

A <u>hive</u> *(n)* is a home for bees. The bees stored honey in their <u>hive</u>.

To <u>disappear</u> *(v)* is to go out of sight or to be lost. Do not <u>disappear</u> when house chores need to be done!

A <u>volcano</u> *(n)* is a mountain with a hole in the middle through which steam, ashes, and hot melted rock, called lava, is pushed out. A <u>volcano</u> in Italy erupted, and the lava flowed out and buried the town.

To <u>tangle</u> *(v)* is to twist and tie together into an untidy mess. Don't let the kitten <u>tangle</u> my ball of yarn!

Choose a word from the word list to solve the crossword puzzle.

ACROSS

2 umbrella-shaped cloth to use when jumping out of a plane

3 mountain that shoots out hot rock, ashes, and steam

5 to go out of sight

8 to twist into an untidy mess

9 material that gives off a sweet smell when burned

DOWN

1 house for bees

2 meal to be eaten outdoors

4 person whose job is to clean, fill, or repair teeth

6 cloth with a special pattern to represent a nation or organization

7 musical instrument

Fill-in-the-Blanks

Fill in the blank with a word from the word list.

The families have a _ at the park every Friday.	1.
During World War II, my grandpa was forced to jump from his plane using a _.	2.
Dr. Brown, our _, checks our teeth for cavities and cleans them every year.	3.
The apostles watched as Jesus began to ascend and _ into the clouds.	4.
The big, black bear was attacked by bees as he ate honey from a _.	5.
Comb your hair every day or it will _ and be very hard to comb.	6.
Maria's family is from Mexico, so she has a Mexican _ in her room.	7.
Many Christians were killed by the Romans for refusing to burn _ to the pagan gods.	8.
The hot, melted rock that shoots out of a _ is called "lava."	9.
In the band, one person played drums, two played guitars, and the fourth person played a _.	10.

Word Usage

Circle the letter next to the sentence that uses the word correctly.

1. (a) A bee's **hive** has many small holes where the honey is stored.
   (b) The shelf was too **hive** for Judy to reach.

2. (a) The other car hit ours and left a **dentist** in our bumper.
   (b) The **dentist** found a cavity in one of my back teeth.

3. (a) It was late, and she was too **tangled** to think of the right answer.
   (b) Be sure to pack the yarn so it will not **tangle**.

4. (a) **Incense** rising up to the sky is a symbol of our prayer rising up to God.
   (b) The delicious chicken baking in the oven gave off an **incense** smell.

5. (a) The meat will **disappear** as soon as we give it to those hungry dogs.
   (b) The teacher told me to **disappear** the words with my crayons.

6. (a) I turned the **banjo** on to hear my favorite folk music.
   (b) That band played songs with the **banjo**, cello, harmonica, and violin.

7. (a) The car got a **flag** tire when it ran over the big nail.
   (b) The American **flag** has fifty stars for each of the fifty states.

8. (a) When the pilot is ready, the airplane will **parachute** into the sky.
   (b) Each person in the airplane has a **parachute** in case of danger.

9. (a) The students collected ash from a **volcano** as part of their science field trip.
   (b) There was a **volcano** of ashes left where we had made the bonfire.

10. (a) We will not have a **picnic** today since it is raining.
    (b) I will help you **picnic** the food for dinner today.

Lesson 22: Word List

ache	fleece	aisle	target	bead
volunteer	cactus	kneel	blacksmith	wigwam

To <u>ache</u> *(v)* is to feel a dull, steady pain. My feet always <u>ache</u> after a long hike.

To <u>volunteer</u> *(v)* is to freely offer to do something, usually a work of charity. John likes to <u>volunteer</u> to help collect shoes for the needy.

<u>Fleece</u> *(n)* is the wool that covers a sheep. My blanket is made of <u>fleece</u>; it keeps me warm on cold nights.

A <u>cactus</u> *(n)* is a plant with a fleshy stem and prickles instead of leaves; grows in dry, hot places. Don't prick your finger on the sharp spikes of the <u>cactus</u>.

An <u>aisle</u> *(n)* is a narrow walkway, often between rows of seats such as in a church. The priest carried the cross down the main <u>aisle</u> of the church to the altar.

To <u>kneel</u> *(v)* is to get down on one's knees. We <u>kneel</u> before Jesus in the Blessed Sacrament as a sign of reverence.

A <u>target</u> *(n)* is a mark that is aimed for and shot at; usually marked with round circles. Robin Hood shot his arrow into the center of the <u>target</u>.

A <u>blacksmith</u> *(n)* is a man who works with iron; he mends tools and shoes horses. The <u>blacksmith</u> made a new suit of armor for the knight.

A <u>bead</u> *(n)* is a small, usually round object with a hole in it through which a string can be passed. The Our Father <u>bead</u> on the rosary was red.

A <u>wigwam</u> *(n)* is a small dwelling used by American Indians; an arched frame of poles covered with animal hides. The Indian family covered their <u>wigwam</u> with buffalo hides.

Puzzle

Choose a word from the word list to solve the crossword puzzle.

ACROSS

2 American Indian dwelling
5 wool that covers a sheep
6 man who works with iron
10 long, narrow walkway

DOWN

1 mark to aim and shoot at
3 plant with prickles
4 freely offer to do something
7 to feel a dull, steady pain
8 to get down on one's knees
9 small, round object with a hole in it

Fill-in-the-Blanks

Fill in the blank with a word from the word list.

In the spring, farmers cut the _ off their sheep to sell for warm jackets.	1. _____
A _ works with iron by heating it in the fire and hammering it into a particular shape.	2. _____
After Christmas Mass, I will _ in front of the Nativity manger to pray.	3. _____
The boys practiced shooting their arrows at the _ they placed on a nearby tree.	4. _____
A prayer is said on each _ of the rosary.	5. _____
My mom went through every _ in the grocery store before she was finished shopping.	6. _____
St. Maximilian Kolbe said he would _ to take the place of another man to save the man's life.	7. _____
My dentist said if my tooth continued to _, I should make a new appointment.	8. _____
The Indian family from the Great Plains used buffalo hides to cover the _ and to make warm clothes.	9. _____
A _ does not need as much water as other plants.	10. _____

Circle the letter next to the sentence that uses the word correctly.

1. (a) The middle ring of a **target** is called the bull's-eye.
   (b) The **target** on the clothes say how much they cost.

2. (a) Carol wore a white **wigwam** to look like an old lady in the play.
   (b) The Indian family stayed warm in the **wigwam** as the winter winds blew.

3. (a) Fr. Carr and the altar boys processed down the middle **aisle** of the church.
   (b) The children brought their rackets and balls to play in the tennis **aisle**.

4. (a) St. Thérèse would move a sacrifice **bead** each time she did a good deed.
   (b) Each pea plant in the garden has a **bead**.

5. (a) The Saguaro is a giant **cactus** that grows as high as sixty feet.
   (b) The thorns on that plant were very sharp and **cactus**.

6. (a) For this activity, you can draw a **volunteer** to connect the dots.
   (b) The children **volunteer** to sing at the nursing home every Christmas.

7. (a) Dad bought me a white coat made of **fleece**.
   (b) "Keep scrubbing the wall until all the **fleece** comes off."

8. (a) The **blacksmith** will shine and polish our shoes with his special cloth.
   (b) The **blacksmith** used tongs to lift and hold the hot iron.

9. (a) Those socks made a red **ache** on her feet because they were too tight.
   (b) My stomach begins to **ache** when I get very hungry.

10. (a) He had to **kneel** down to pick the strawberries hidden under the leaves.
    (b) I was much taller when I stood up on the **kneel**.

| boulder | grin | evacuate | mansion | whittle |
| detour | cellar | pew | brand | jester |

A **boulder** *(n)* is a huge, round rock lying on the surface of the ground or stuck in the soil. Kevin climbed over the **boulder** that had rolled down the hill.

A **detour** *(n)* is another road for traveling when the usual one cannot be used. While work was being done on the main road, we took a **detour** around the town.

A **grin** *(n)* is a wide smile, often showing teeth. The cowboy gave a **grin** of delight when he saw the pony.

A **cellar** *(n)* is an area, usually under a house, mostly used for storing food and equipment. The wealthy prince kept his wine in the **cellar** of his castle.

To **evacuate** *(v)* is to move out of danger. The people of the town will **evacuate** if the river floods its banks.

A **pew** *(n)* is a long, fixed bench that faces the altar in a church. George Washington sat in the front **pew** and prayed for the safety of his soldiers.

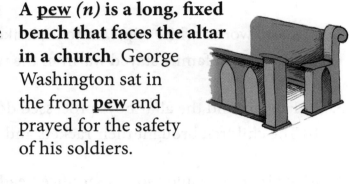

A **mansion** *(n)* is a large, expensive house. The southern family's **mansion** was destroyed during the Civil War.

A **brand** *(n)* is a category or kind of product identified by name as being made by a certain producer. Dad ate his favorite **brand** of ham.

To **whittle** *(v)* is to cut or shape wood with a knife. The artist wanted to **whittle** the odd piece of wood into a figure of a dog.

A **jester** *(n)* was a person or clown who amused a king or queen. A **jester** would wear bright-colored clothes, juggle, and play music for the king and queen.

Choose a word from the word list to solve the crossword puzzle.

ACROSS

1 long fixed bench in a church
4 large house
7 another road to travel
8 person who entertains a king or queen
9 show the teeth in a wide smile
10 underground room for storing things

DOWN

2 move out of danger
3 huge rock
5 to shape wood with a knife
6 category or kind of product

Fill in the blank with a word from the word list.

Every _ in the church was filled for Sunday Mass.	1.
Dad had to take a _ to work because all the main roads were flooded.	2.
The rich man owned a beautiful _ which he turned into an art gallery.	3.
Which _ of oatmeal should we buy?	4.
Patsy took a picture of Grandpa with a big _ on his face and then framed it for Grandma.	5.
The hikers were trying to figure out how to climb around the huge _ in their path.	6.
The National Weather Service told everyone in New Orleans to _ because of the coming hurricane.	7.
Grandfather learned to _ little, wooden toy soldiers to give to his grandchildren.	8.
We called my brother a _ because he was always clowning around to make us laugh.	9.
The family stored crates of fruit and vegetables in the cool _ to eat during the winter.	10.

Word Usage

Replace the words in bold with the correct word from the word list.

We had difficulty climbing around a **large rock** on the mountain path.	1.
"John, can you get me a few potatoes from the **underground room used for storing food**?"	2.
The little girl in the hospital gave me a big **wide smile** when I brought her the baby doll.	3.
It is much longer to take the **alternate road** when the usual one cannot be used.	4.
We always genuflect in front of the Blessed Sacrament before going into our **wooden bench.**	5.
The American Heritage Society purchased the **large, expensive house** for an American history museum.	6.
The Steinway piano is a very well-made **certain kind of product** that has a beautiful, rich sound.	7.
Everyone should **move out of danger** the house as fast as they can if a fire breaks out.	8.
While the royal dinner was being served, a **person to amuse a king** began to entertain the court.	9.
We watched the talented boy **cut and shape wood with a knife** pieces of wood into small animals.	10.

Lesson 24: Word List

chimney	quill	zigzag	diamond	improve
label	canal	spade	deacon	hook

A <u>chimney</u> *(n)* is a tall, hollow, narrow passage for carrying smoke from a fireplace to the outdoors. A fireplace <u>chimney</u> should be cleaned each year.

A <u>label</u> *(n)* is a piece of paper attached to an object that tells something about it. Please read the <u>label</u> on the jelly jar to see how much sugar it contains.

A <u>quill</u> *(n)* is a stiff feather from a large bird. People used a <u>quill</u> for writing with ink before the metal pen was invented.

A <u>canal</u> *(n)* is a waterway dug to allow ships to cross through land. The Erie <u>Canal</u> is a waterway connection between the Atlantic Ocean and the Great Lakes.

A <u>zigzag</u> *(n)* is a line that goes sharply from side to side. The ship sailed in a <u>zigzag</u> to avoid the enemy submarines.

A <u>spade</u> *(n)* is a tool for digging, with a pointed end and a handle. Dad used a <u>spade</u> to dig a garden.

A <u>diamond</u> *(n)* is a valuable, clear stone, often put in rings or necklaces. A large <u>diamond</u> adorned the crown on Our Lady's statue.

A <u>deacon</u> *(n)* is a man ordained to assist a priest in the work of the Church. St. Philip was the first <u>deacon</u> mentioned in the Bible.

To <u>improve</u> *(v)* is to become better or to make better. You can <u>improve</u> your handwriting if you practice writing neatly.

A <u>hook</u> *(n)* is a curved, stiff object used for catching or hanging something. A <u>hook</u> is usually made of a strong material like metal.

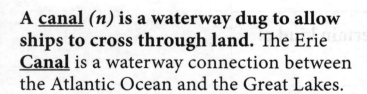

Puzzle

Choose a word from the word list to solve the crossword puzzle.

ACROSS

4 to make or become better
6 waterway for ships and boats to cross land
8 hollow passage built to carry smoke outdoors
9 stiff feather from a large bird
10 tool for digging

DOWN

1 curved, stiff object used for hanging objects
2 line that moves sharply from side to side
3 man who assists a priest
5 piece of paper attached to an object that tells about it
7 valuable, clear stone

Fill-in-the-Blanks

Fill in the blank with a word from the word list.

Thomas Jefferson wrote the *Declaration of Independence* with a _ and ink.	1. _____
The lightning flashed across the sky in the shape of a _.	2. _____
The first martyr, St. Stephen, was a holy _ who assisted the apostles with their work.	3. _____
Dad attached a _ on the back of the door for me to hang my coat.	4. _____
Don't burn evergreens in a fireplace because their sappy smoke makes the _ sticky and dirty.	5. _____
The violin teacher told Ann to practice every day to _ her playing.	6. _____
The Panama _ is a very important man-made waterway that connects the Atlantic Ocean to the Pacific Ocean.	7. _____
If you do not put a _ on the salt container, someone might think it is sugar.	8. _____
Our family saw a large, sparkling _ in a glass case at the science museum.	9. _____
It was hard work to dig up the big garden with a _.	10. _____

Word Usage

Circle the letter next to the sentence that uses the word correctly.

1. (a) The man built steps over his **canal** so no one would walk on his neat lawn.
   (b) A **canal** was dug to allow ships to pass from the ocean to the river.

2. (a) The lumber men will **spade** the large logs into the river.
   (b) The boys used a **spade** to dig a long hole for the pipes.

3. (a) **Deacon** McGuirk assisted Father Jones at Mass.
   (b) The bright **deacon** led the ships safely to the harbor.

4. (a) I trained my dog to **improve** to me his paw.
   (b) You can **improve** your manners by thinking more of others.

5. (a) The monks copied the entire Bible, each using a **quill** and ink.
   (b) Jessica used a **quill** to stir the boiling onion soup.

6. (a) My uncle showed me how to attach a worm on the **hook** of my fishing line.
   (b) Joshua screwed a **hook** onto his pajamas so he could hang them in the closet.

7. (a) The produce department is required to put a **label** on each fruit container.
   (b) My little sister begged me to read her a bedtime **label**.

8. (a) Baby Grace likes to draw a **zigzag** on every page of her coloring book.
   (b) My hair is **zigzag** when I first wake up in the morning.

9. (a) The man lived in the **chimney** because he liked to smoke his pipe every day.
   (b) Mr. McMahon showed Tommy how to clean the old **chimney**.

10. (a) The **diamond** in Mother's ring is so sparkly!
    (b) The children picked the ripe **diamond** from the garden.

VOCABULARY 3
ANSWER KEY

Week 1, Day 3
1. weasel
2. copperhead
3. torch
4. greedy
5. heron
6. whirlpool
7. drizzle
8. eel
9. station
10. tower

Week 1, Day 4
[this exercise has no numbers]
1. a
2. b
3. a
4. b
5. b
6. a
7. b
8. a
9. b
10. b

Week 2, Day 3
1. jacket
2. opossum
3. bishop
4. ladder
5. raft
6. cherry
7. arrow
8. eager
9. canary
10. flute

Week 2, Day 4
1. canary
2. flute

3. arrow
4. bishop
5. raft
6. jacket
7. cherry
8. ladder
9. eager
10. opossum

Week 3, Day 3
1. fasten
2. kite
3. candle
4. nutcracker
5. bamboo
6. gnat
7. chipmunk
8. herd
9. antenna
10. badger

Week 3, Day 4
1. b
2. a
3. b
4. b
5. a
6. b
7. b
8. a
9. a
10. a

Week 4, Day 3
1. doubt
2. weapon
3. crucifix
4. magnet

5. crate
6. visor
7. haul
8. trade
9. poet
10. creek

Week 4, Day 4
1. b
2. b
3. a
4. a
5. b
6. a
7. a
8. a
9. b
10. a

Week 5, Day 3
1. author
2. chapter
3. collect
4. rainbow
5. hummingbird
6. rapidly
7. traitor
8. halo
9. weep
10. donkey

Week 5, Day 4
1. author
2. hummingbird
3. collect
4. weep
5. traitor
6. chapter
7. donkey
8. rapidly

9. rainbow
10. halo

Week 6, Day 3
1. drill
2. harp
3. octopus
4. nibble
5. pure
6. hut
7. igloo
8. resurrect
9. stake
10. concert

Week 6, Day 4
1. octopus
2. harp
3. concert
4. resurrect
5. drill
6. nibble
7. stake
8. igloo
9. pure
10. hut

Week 10, Day 3
1. caterpillar
2. shabby
3. oval
4. medal
5. acrobat
6. blessing
7. crow
8. spoil
9. vigil
10. hawk

Week 10, Day 4
1. a
2. b
3. a
4. a
5. b
6. a
7. a
8. b
9. a
10. a

Week 11, Day 3
1. needle
2. raw

3. virtue
4. mint
5. widow
6. choir
7. paste
8. tremble
9. monastery
10. stream

Week 11, Day 4
1. mint
2. raw
3. monastery
4. choir
5. needle
6. paste
7. virtue
8. stream
9. tremble
10. widow

Week 12, Day 3
1. orchard
2. carpenter
3. scoop
4. loaf
5. clay
6. cashew
7. mayor
8. wren
9. ruler
10. sacrifice

Week 12, Day 4
1. a
2. b
3. b
4. a
5. a
6. b
7. a
8. b
9. b
10. b

Week 13, Day 3
1. pave
2. roast
3. confess
4. marble
5. elastic
6. famous
7. panda
8. praise
9. soar
10. gallop

Week 13, Day 4
b
a
a
b
a
a
a
b
a
a

Week 14, Day 3
1. acorn
2. dough
3. grace
4. wasp
5. scatter
6. harvest
7. symbol
8. tomahawk
9. caravan
10. eternal

Week 14, Day 4
1. caravan
2. symbol
3. scatter
4. acorn
5. grace
6. wasp
7. tomahawk
8. eternal
9. dough
10. harvest

Week 15, Day 3
1. route
2. ripe
3. peddler
4. duet
5. lizard
6. award
7. feast
8. sorrow
9. leash
10. manhole

Week 15, Day 4
1. b
2. a
3. a
4. b
5. b
6. a
7. a

8. a
9. b
10. a

Week 19, Day 3
1. breeze
2. barrel
3. angle
4. yard
5. consecrate
6. treasure
7. ink
8. fawn
9. ramble
10. feather

Week 19, Day 4
1. b
2. b
3. a
4. a
5. b
6. a
7. b
8. a
9. a
10. a

Week 20, Day 3
1. apron
2. adult
3. apostle
4. island
5. lantern
6. orphan
7. shiver
8. chalice
9. dozen
10. saddle

Week 20, Day 4
1. dozen
2. saddle
3. chalice
4. island
5. lantern
6. apostle
7. orphan
8. adult
9. apron
10. shiver

Week 21, Day 3
1. character
2. reptile
3. angel
4. cradle

5. ostrich
6. Mercy
7. create
8. harbor
9. soak
10. ladle

Week 21, Day 4
1. b
2. b
3. a
4. a
5. b
6. a
7. a
8. b
9. a
10. b

Week 22, Day 3
1. burglar
2. procession
3. dairy
4. glossary
5. band
6. whiskers
7. warehouse
8. chorus
9. miracle
10. chimpanzee

Week 22, Day 4
1. a
2. a
3. a
4. a
5. a
6. a
7. a
8. b
9. a
10. a

Week 23, Day 3
1. season
2. echo
3. skim
4. universe
5. soul
6. bulldozer
7. bait
8. crack
9. tithe
10. Salmon

Week 23, Day 4
1. universe
2. bait
3. skim
4. crack
5. echo
6. tithe
7. soul
8. season
9. salmon
10. bulldozer

Week 24, Day 3
1. chest
2. divine
3. marry
4. cottage
5. habit
6. respect
7. stilts
8. increase
9. frustrated
10. beaver

Week 24, Day 4
1. b
2. b
3. a
4. b
5. b
6. a
7. b
8. a
9. a
10. b

Week 28, Day 3
1. serpent
2. code
3. attach
4. relic
5. hoof
6. ankle
7. shrine
8. steam
9. balcony
10. float

Week 28, Day 4
1. b
2. a
3. a
4. a
5. b
6. a
7. b

8. b
9 a
10. b

Week 29, Day 3
1. wisp
2. harmony
3. tongs
4. sacristy
5. whale
6. ornament
7. moat
8. hose
9. vestments
10. margin

Week 29, Day 4
1. ornament
2. sacristy
3. moat
4. margin
5. whale
6. wisp
7. Vestments
8. harmony
9. hose
10. tongs

Week 30, Day 3
1. picnic
2. parachute
3. dentist
4. disappear
5. hive
6. tangle
7. flag
8. incense
9. volcano
10. banjo

Week 30, Day 4
1. a
2. b
3. b

4. a
5. a
6. b
7. b
8. b
9. a
10. a

Week 31, Day 3
1. fleece
2. blacksmith
3. kneel
4. target
5. bead
6. aisle
7. volunteer
8. ache
9. wigwam
10. cactus

Week 31, Day 4
1. a
2. b
3. a
4. a
5. a
6. b
7. a
8. b
9. b
10. a

Week 32, Day 3
1. pew
2. detour
3. mansion
4. brand
5. grin
6. boulder
7. evacuate
8. whittle
9. jester
10. cellar

Week 32, Day 4
1. boulder
2. cellar
3. grin
4. detour
5. pew
6. mansion
7. brand
8. evacuate
9. jester
10. whittle

Week 33, Day 3
1. quill
2. zigzag
3. deacon
4. hook
5. chimney
6. improve
7. Canal
8. label
9. diamond
10. spade

Week 33, Day 4
1. b
2. b
3. a
4. b
5. a
6. a
7. a
8. a
9. b
10. a

VOCABULARY 3 WORD LIST

A

ACHE
ACORN
ACROBAT
ADULT
AISLE
ANGEL
ANGLE
ANKLE
ANTENNA
APOSTLE
APRON
ARROW
ATTACH
AUTHOR
AWARD

B

BADGER
BAIT
BALCONY
BAMBOO
BAND
BANJO
BARREL
BEAD
BEAVER
BEELINE
BISHOP
BLACKSMITH
BLESSING
BOULDER
BRAND
BREEZE
BULLDOZER
BURGLAR

C

CACTUS
CANAL
CANARY
CANDLE
CARAVAN
CARPENTER
CASHEW
CATERPILLAR
CELLAR
CHALICE
CHAPTER
CHERRY
CHEST
CHIMNEY
CHIMPANZEE
CHIPMUNK
CHOIR
CLAY
CODE
COLLECT

CONCERT
CONSECRATE
COPPERHEAD
COTTAGE
CRACK
CRADLE
CRATE
CRAWL
CRAYFISH
CREEK
CROW
CRUCIFIX
CYMBAL

D

DAIRY
DEACON
DENTIST
DETOUR
DIAMOND
DISAPPEAR
DIVINE
DONKEY
DOUGH
DOZEN
DRAMA
DRILL
DRIZZLE
DUET

E

ECHO
EEL
ELASTIC
EMPTY
ETERNAL
EVACUATE

F

FAMOUS
FASTEN
FAWN
FEAST
FEATHER
FLAG
FLEECE
FLOAT
FLUFFY
FLUTE
FRUSTRATE

G

GALLOP
GILD
GNAT
GRACE
GRIN

H

HABIT
HALO
HAMMER
HANDY
HARBOR
HARP
HARVEST
HAUL
HAWK
HERON
HIVE
HOOF
HOOK
HORN
HOSE
HUMMINGBIRD
HUT

I

IGLOO
IMPROVE
INCENSE
INK
ISLAND

J

JACKET
JESTER

K

KITE
KNEEL
KNIFE
KNOB

L

LABEL
LADDER
LADLE
LANTERN
LEASH
LIZARD
LOAF

M

MAGNET
MANHOLE
MARBLE
MARGIN
MARRY
MEDAL
MERCY
MINT
MIRACLE
MOAT
MONASTERY

N

NEEDLE
NOTCH
NUTCRACKER

O

OCTOPUS
OPOSSUM
ORCHARD
ORNAMENT
ORPHAN
OSTRICH
OVAL

P

PANDA
PARACHUTE
PASTE
PAVE
PEDDLER
PEW
PICNIC
POET
PRAISE
PROCESSION
PURE

Q

QUILL

R

RAFT
RAINBOW
RAMBLE
RAPIDLY
RAW
RELIC
REPTILE

RESURRECT
RIPE
ROAST
ROUTE
RUG
RULER

S

SACRIFICE
SACRISTY
SADDLE
SALMON
SCOOP
SCULPTOR
SEASON
SERPENT
SHABBY
SHINE
SHIVER
SHRINE
SIFT
SKIM
SOAK
SORROW
SOUL
SPADE
SPOIL
STAKE
STARE
STATION
STEAM
STILTS
STREAM
SYMBOL

T

TANGLE
TARGET

TITHE
TOMAHAWK
TONGS
TORCH
TOWER
TRADE
TRAITOR
TREASURE
TRELLIS

V

VESTMENT
VIGIL
VIRTUE
VISOR
VOLCANO

W

WAREHOUSE
WASP
WEAPON
WEASEL
WEEP
WHALE
WHIRLPOOL
WHISKER
WHITTLE
WIDOW
WIGWAM
WISP
WREN

Y

YARD

Z

ZIGZAG